Developing Management Potential

DATE DUE			
10/11/16			
2 JAN 2019			

Developing Management Potential

How to lead, motivate and support care teams effectively

Adrian Ashurst RGN.DMS

QUAY
BOOKS

A division of MA Healthcare Ltd

Quay Books Division, MA Healthcare Ltd, St Jude's Church, Dulwich Road, London
SE24 0PB

British Library Cataloguing-in-Publication Data
A catalogue record is available for this book

© MA Healthcare Limited 2010

ISBN-10: 1 85642 402 2
ISBN-13: 978 1 85642 402 8

Printed by CLE, Huntingdon, Cambridgeshire

To Brittany and Reece
This book is dedicated to you both
Your unconditional love helps to inspire me to write
Thank you for your sense of humour, patience and support
All my love
Adrian

Foreword

I first worked with Adrian when he was a regional operations manager with Highfield (NHP) in 2001. He had his first book – *Positive Customer Care: an Aide Memoire* – published in 2002 by Quay Books. This proved very popular with our staff at the time.

Working with Dr Richard Hawkins he edited *How to Be a Great Care Assistant* published by Hawker Publications in June 2006. Adrian has also written *Managing a Care Home*, published by Quay Books in 2006.

Adrian has had a successful nursing and management career spanning over three decades, working for the National Health Service until 1989. He has held a number of senior management posts working with several national independent care providers throughout the United Kingdom, including Highbank Healthcare, Robinia, Craegmoor Healthcare, Hallmark Healthcare and NHP's Highfield Care, and he is currently the Training Manager for Cambian Healthcare, the country's leading provider of intensive psychiatric rehabilitation.

In addition, Adrian spent three years working as a brain injury case manager working with clients and their families throughout England and Wales. In 2006 he joined Cambian Healthcare in a consultancy position, quickly becoming our Relationships Manager. Through his knowledge of healthcare and Cambian in particular, he took over the vital role of Training Manager.

Adrian delivers Active Care and other training courses. He also manages the extensive training programmes available for Cambian's registered nurses and existing and future care workers.

I am sure that you will greatly enjoy reading his new book and gain a useful insight into the world of management, especially within the independent care sector.

Mike McQuaid
Chief Operation Officer, The Cambian Group

Contents

Contents

Chapter 11
The future challenges

Afterword

Index

Introduction

Today, working within the independent care sector, we are faced with a number of complex and difficult challenges when it comes to the delivery of high standards of care and hotel service in the middle of a credit crunch and a deep recession that affects the whole of the country.

When I qualified as a staff nurse many years ago, I could never find a book that explained how to become a better staff nurse and eventually climb the management ladder. There were lots of clinical books available, but few that were written for prospective managers of the future.

I have based much of this book on my personal experiences and I have used some previously published articles and editorials from the journal *Nursing & Residential Care*. I am privileged to have been their Consultant Editor for the last ten years.

The book has been written to encourage readers to examine their own personal professional development.

I have included a number of discussion points which are designed to facilitate discussion and debate between managers and their colleagues. These can also be used as part of staff meetings and or as an integral part of staff training sessions.

Key points form a basic component of some of the chapters, highlighted to encourage further reading and research.

Chapter 1: Where are you now?

This chapter highlights the importance of promoting a positive image in nursing today and also raises the question: Are you fit for the future?

Career development remains at the centre of the book's value; therefore I feel it is important to reflect on the first staff nurse job.

Chapter 2: Developing your management skills

I ask the question 'Is your management up to scratch?'. We often take our managers for granted, but we must all keep ourselves updated and able to deal with day-to-day issues that can arise in any care environment.

There is a section on budgets – a simple guide which will prove useful for those managers without a background in finance. Balancing the care home or independent hospital budget has now become pivotal to the success or failure of any care business.

Time management is very important if we are to achieve a good work–life balance, and poor time management can often lead to a breakdown in relationships.

I conclude this chapter by looking at a number of recognised business management styles.

Chapter 3: Improving your communications

In order to improve your communication skills you need to be able to deliver exciting presentations and be able to speak in public. I believe we can learn from the NHS, and likewise I feel that they can also learn many things from the independent care sector.

Chapter 4: Recruiting and managing staff

This chapter deals with some of the most important aspects of the care home manager's role today. Effective staff recruitment and selection ensure that we can build excellent multidisciplinary teams which can provide our residents/patients with the best care and services available.

I also explore the staff supervision/appraisal systems and the preceptorship process. I raise the question about who cares for staff during suspension. This is a sensitive subject, but I feel strongly that we should address this matter.

There is a section on managing difficult people.

Chapter 5: Marketing a care home or care facility

Marketing your care home remains at the top of the agenda when it comes to being a successful manager. Poor marketing can result in a drop in referrals and lots of empty beds.

A successful marketing campaign can result in a full care home plus a healthy waiting list for people wishing to be placed in your care home.

You must also recognise the power of the media if you are to make the most of public relation (PR) opportunities. Promoting your care home in the local community is essential if you desire to raise your profile and enhance your reputation amongst your neighbours.

Chapter 6: Current management challenges

This chapter looks at rehabilitation for older people, mental health issues and making mealtimes memorable. In addition I raise the question: Who pays for wasted medicines? I also discuss religion in a care setting. Is this a private matter?

Chapter 7: Building relationships

This chapter explores the importance of being able to build sustainable relations with outside agencies and how to successfully handle people's complaints.

Providing support for relatives is a foundation stone of any successful care setting.

Chapter 8: Refurbishment projects

From personal experience I am able to discuss some of the issues surrounding successful refurbishment projects. I also discuss working with architects and building contractors.

Chapter 9: Health and Safety in the care home

This chapter covers the basic components of the manager's role in respect of health and safety (H&S).

Because there are so many changes in this area it is vital that care home managers keep themselves up to date with current H&S legislation by regularly visiting the Health and Safety Executive website for new information.

Chapter 10: Sharing best practice

In order for any care provider organisation to grow we need to lead, motivate and support our staff. This chapter looks at promoting care homes and issues surrounding advocacy and the Mental Capacity Act.

Chapter 11: The future care challenges

In this chapter I look into the future of nursing and consider the impact upon nurse education, with the expectation that from 2013 all nurses will be educated to degree level.

Finally I look at the clinical governance process and the importance of managers being able to audit not only clinical practice but also their business.

Summary

It is essential that care home and independent hospital managers are equipped to face the challenges set by government and the Care Quality Commission (CQC).

Whilst training remains vitally important in developing new managers I believe that there is a need for a book which can act as an *aide memoire* for those who aspire to senior management positions.

I believe that successful managers possess similar personal characteristics, and throughout my nursing and management career I have learned a great deal from my mentors, which I still remember clearly after all these years.

Customer service

For the last twenty years in the pursuit of my management career within the independent care sector, I have spent a great deal of my time travelling throughout England and Wales, sometimes staying overnight in a variety of small bed and breakfast establishments and a cross section of hotels.

I am amazed at how much I have learned from watching the manner in which hotel staff deliver their customer service – how they actually deal with difficult people, how some staff and managers go the extra mile.

I believe that everyone who aspires to become a manager should take a leaf out of the book of successful hotel groups by continuing to improve endeavour to improve the environment of care facilities and at the same time develop their staff team.

This approach can only help to enhance the reputation of care facilities and improve their occupancy where appropriate.

Today there are thousands of people searching the Internet every day for a care placement either for themselves (for a family member) or a client, if they are purchasing care on behalf of an individual.

It is now recognised that customers have become much more discerning and as a result their expectations are much higher than ever before. As a direct result, the National Health Service (NHS) and the independent care sector have had to develop and improve their hotel services and delivery of care, from the types of food provided to the continuing cleanliness of the environment.

The manager's main aim must always be to meet the individual's social and clinical needs whilst engaging with the resident's families and funders.

I hope you enjoy reading this book and that it makes you stop and think that we all have a very special 'duty of care' for those people less fortunate than ourselves.

Author's note

Throughout the book, where I refer to care homes, this is a generic term that can be used for independent hospitals, specialist hospitals and other types of care establishment. Whilst emphasis may be placed on the care of older people, this book is designed for nurses and senior carers working with patients and residents.

Acknowledgements

There are far too many colleagues that I have enjoyed working with since commencing my nursing and management career as a student nurse at Salford Royal Hospital in January 1971 to name them all individually. However, there are some special people who deserve a mention, including my parents, my brothers and sister; Stephen, Carole and Paul and their families for their love; plus my friends including Beryl, Graham, Maggie, Karen, Kate, Jan, Lisa, Claire, Jane, Kerrie, Melissa, Stephen, Emily, Roisin, Simon and Sue for their support.

Thanks to Malcolm Kelshaw and Elizabeth Wagstaff for believing in me and giving me the opportunity to develop my successful nursing and business management career. I learned so much from Elizabeth including the necessity as a manager to always ensure that 'your ducks are in a row' before making a decision. Her passion, enthusiasm, professionalism, knowledge and experience taught me always to search and work hard for your success. Her great example and words of wisdom have always stayed with me.

Thanks must go to the *Nursing & Residential Care* editors, including Laura Dean Osgood and the NRC Board members.

Thanks to Ian and Bruce at Clear Creative, for their special artistic and design assistance over the last fifteen years.

Thanks to Alison, Tracey, Gretchen and Jennie for proofreading, plus Julie for typing the manuscript.

Thanks to Maria and Thu at Quay Books who have provided much professional guidance and support in making this book become a reality.

Thanks to everyone at the Cambian Group, including Saleem, Tony, John, Jenny, Laura, Barrie, Nick, Heather, Julie, Sarah and all the hospital managers, including Ricky, Nita, Alyson, Victor, Albert, Paul, Angela, Charles, Robert and Keith, plus their administrators, multidisciplinary team members, the operational team, support staff and finally Mike McQuaid for writing the foreword to this my latest book.

Adrian M. Ashurst
March 2010

CHAPTER I

Where are you now?

Promoting a positive image

It's becoming a real challenge to attract the right people into the nursing profession. The perception of nursing as a vocational career appears to have changed over the last decade. Some are using nursing as a stepping stone to further their academic goals. However, those who decide to embark upon a nursing career need to demonstrate total commitment and appreciate the responsibility and accountability necessary to fulfil the role.

I believe the manner in which nurses portray themselves can have far-reaching consequences, not only for themselves but the reputation of their place of work.

Rosemary Kennedy – Chief Nursing Officer for Wales – recently commented on the recruitment of nurses:

Attracting and selecting highly motivated people into nursing is vital. I was, therefore, disappointed to be told by a student nurse that she regarded her training as a mere stop-gap, something to occupy her before making up her mind about what she really wanted to do (Kennedy, 2009).

I recognise that nursing is often challenging and sometimes stressful, but nurses must always be prepared to abide by the NMC's professional Code of Conduct.

The NMC has said that:

We remind nurses and midwives that they are personally accountable for their actions at all times, including how they behave in their personal life. It is important to remember that you are equally responsible for upholding The Code in your personal and professional life (NMC, 2008).

This holds true when nurses use social networking sites such as Facebook.

The NMC (2008) has provided nurses with advice regarding this:

Used properly, these websites are a great way to find old friends, join interest groups and share information.

However, nurses and midwives should remember that anything posted on a social networking site is in the public domain.

What may be considered to be letting off steam about a work situation, can potentially be read by someone who may take offence at the content of a posting.

Nurses could be risking their registration if posting inappropriate comments about colleagues or patients, or posting any material that could be deemed explicit (NMC, 2008).

Nurses who use these websites must always use them sensibly; however, those nurses who choose to misuse the service should be disciplined in accordance with the local policy.

References

Ashurst, A. (2009) Promoting a positive image. *Nursing & Residential Care*, **11**(11), 535.

Kennedy, R. (2009) Notes from a CNO. *NMC News*, Issue 29.

Nursing and Midwifery Council (2008) *Your Code of Conduct applies to your personal life*. NMC, London. Available online at: http://www.nmc-uk.org/.

Discussion points

■ How can we attract the right people into the nursing profession?
■ Discuss the various challenges that affect nurses today.
■ Why is it important for nurses and carers to use great caution when using Facebook, Twitter and other social networking sites?

Are you fit for the future?

Despite the country's economic downturn, felt by many people, a New Year brings us all the opportunity for a fresh start. I have already noticed how many of my friends and colleagues have signed up for new gym memberships, although sadly – if past records are to be repeated – most will lose their initial enthusiasm by early spring and their attendance at the gym will diminish rapidly.

How many of us complain about putting on weight? Yet still we continue to enjoy all the things we are advised not to eat – plus the lack of exercise. Leading a balanced lifestyle and retaining or improving your physical fitness may result in you feeling less stressed, more energetic and ready to face the challenges presented at work and home.

Staff working in any type of care environment should be willing to set an example to those we care for by supporting their quest to eat more healthily and take regular exercise.

As well as keeping physically fit, I believe that we also need to recognise the importance of keeping ourselves up to date with nursing research, legislation and scientific breakthroughs surrounding the care of people, including those suffering with mental health needs and learning disabilities.

Is the concept of 'lifelong learning' a myth or reality in our care homes today? Nurses must keep themselves up to date if they wish to continue practising as registered nurses in this country; therefore, lifelong learning must become a reality.

The Nursing and Midwifery Council (NMC) (2005) states that

> Registered nurses need to meet the NMC post-registration education and practice (PREP) continuing professional development (CPD) standard which is to:
>
> ■ Undertake at least five days or 35 hours of learning activity relevant to your practice during the three years prior to your renewal of registration.
> ■ Maintain a personal professional profile (PPP) of your learning activity.
> ■ Comply with any request from the NMC to audit how you have met these requirements.

Training and ongoing personal development must be at the forefront for all our staff, from the delivery of robust staff induction programmes through to regular in-house training sessions. Staff should be encouraged to undertake their NVQs to raise the clinical and business standards in the care home. Specialist training can be expensive; however, it is a worthwhile long-term investment in our most important asset.

Poorly trained team members may put themselves and their residents at risk if the care home's local policies and procedures are not adhered to. Ignorance cannot be seen as a defence for poor practice; while protecting residents from all forms of abuse, staff must be trained to recognise the 'tell tale' signs displayed by the most vulnerable residents and what to do if they suspect that any form of abuse is taking place.

Registered nurses have a wealth of knowledge that they can pass on to their colleagues, and designing a comprehensive in-house training programme using your own team members will give them confidence and a feeling of being valued. Successful care homes have already adopted these simple steps to improving all their staff's knowledge and I believe that you should share your experience with a much larger audience.

References

Ashurst, A. (2008) Editorial. *Nursing & Residential Care*, **11**(15).
Nursing and Midwifery Council (2005) *The PREP Handbook*. NMC, London.

Discussion points

- Why is a robust staff induction programme very important for all newly appointed members of the care staff team?
- How can you encourage and motivate staff to share their best practice?
- How will you encourage staff to continue to keep themselves updated in their clinical and managerial development?

How do other people see you in your present role?

It is important that you acknowledge what other people think about you in the work place. Three hundred and sixty degree feedback is important between the staff and managers; however it is essential that managers are not found to allow themselves to be managed by the care team.

Your management decisions must be seen as fair. When you are placed in a position to make difficult decisions, think of all the possible outcomes. If you are not sure or confident about your management decisions then you should always seek advice from your line manager. Always think of the worst possible consequence of any of your actions.

Successful managers must be seen to be making a difference, not just attending meetings that at times appear to be held for their own sake. See the case study to examine how quickly things can go wrong in a care setting.

Case study: the Charge Nurse and the wound dressings

As a charge nurse working on a busy medical ward in a large NHS hospital, I was responsible for managing the staff and ensuring the clinical well-being of all the patients on a daily basis.

Every day the tasks were allocated to individual staff at handover, and for several weeks it had become apparent to all the staff that I had not allocated myself to carry out the dressings on a gentleman who was being nursed on a water bed and who had several very large sacral pressure sores with which he had been admitted into hospital with some weeks earlier.

One day, after handover, one of the ward's senior staff nurses came to see me privately and suggested that I should take my turn in undertaking the dressings like everyone else.

The gentleman's sacral dressings took an hour to complete and the odours were overpowering. However, I duly undertook this task on a regular basis and the staff appeared to respect me for taking this decision.

Summary
Had the staff nurse not spoken to me, I would never have known the unrest among the qualified staff that my failure to carry out the dressing regime was causing, and the effect that it was having on my team's overall morale. Always listen to your staff, as they do play an important role in ensuring the cohesiveness of the care team.

Discussion points

- What would have happened to staff morale if the ward charge nurse had decided not to carry out the wound dressings?
- Was the ward charge nurse right to take the decision that he did following the private talks with the senior staff nurse?
- Do the team feel that the charge nurse could have demonstrated his clinical expertise in finding out why the wound was so malodorous, outlining treatment options such as metroniadazole gel or larval therapy to reduce odour and exudate and improve the patient's care?
- This could also have actually demonstrated the true value of the ward manager as a clinician improving patient care and as a manager reducing the staff workload.

Key influencers

There are many people who may influence your career: family, friends, influential care home owners, care home managers and colleagues.

Not everyone is destined to become a manager, but if that is the direction you wish to follow then it is important to get as much experience in either nursing or social care as you can.

Successful managers with a proven clinical caring track record often appear to have greater empathy with their staff than those people who come into care management from a different background. However, there can be some advantages to having spent time outside of the care industry, experiencing different cultures and working practices.

For example, in the past, some students, once they had graduated from university, chose to take a gap year, backpacking around Europe or further afield. Today, in the current difficult economic climate and with students experiencing the effects of the 'credit crunch', this gap year option may not be available.

Where would you eventually like to be in your chosen career?

If you are a staff nurse looking to become a care home or an independent hospital manager, then it would be useful to consider applying for an external business management or skills course.

In addition, you may have gained enough experience to be promoted to the position of Head of Care.

The 'Head of Care' role

This exciting role often combines various management and clinical responsibilities. The post holder has the opportunity to learn how to manage under the watchful eye of a senior and experienced manager.

JOB DESCRIPTION

HEAD OF CARE
Adapted from Cambian Healthcare Ltd, November 2009

Job Title: HEAD OF CARE
Reports to: Care Home/Hospital Manager

Purpose and summary of job:
To oversee/maintain the care of all clients within the Care Home/Hospital and, in the absence of the Care Home/Hospital Manager, take responsibility for the day to day running of the Hospital.

The post holder will provide leadership, direction and supervision to all clinical and support staff. They will provide effective communication to both the care team and Multi-Disciplinary Team, acting as a positive role model at all times. They will contribute to the hospital achieving a high level of staff morale and in developing the service. The post holder will be responsible for implementing and evaluating agreed systems of clinical and operational support, aimed at the continual professional

---

development of the nursing team and delivery of a high level of care to our residents/clients.

Main duties and responsibilities
- **Care**:
    - Oversee the effective admission/discharge of all residents/clients.
    - Ensure that all referrals are adequately assessed with all reports prepared within set time limits, comprehensively and to a high standard. On admission ensure all necessary residents/clients documentation is available.
    - Ensure all social and health needs of the residents/clients are assessed and risks evaluated. To monitor the planning and on-going evaluation of their care, including specific therapeutic interventions.
    - Act as key nurse to designated residents/clients.
    - Take responsibility for client/staff meetings including clinical reviews, handovers and ward rounds.
    - Organise workload by forward planning off duty, ensuring that there is sufficient cover and when necessary deal with problems where appropriate.
    - Ensure duty rotas are produced within set time limits and that all bank and overtime rotas are exhausted prior to using any agency staff.
    - Report any ill-health amongst residents/clients and make requests for General Practitioner (GP) visits where necessary.
    - Responsible for the implementation of risk assessment; risk management and to embed clinical governance practices.
    - Carry out all nursing procedures as and when necessary.
    - Administer prescribed medicines and maintain the necessary records as per guidelines.
    - Practice maximum integrity in all dealings with residents'/clients' personal and financial affairs and avoid abuse of the privileged relationship which exists with residents/clients.
    - Maintain accurate records and ensure that each resident/client within the Care Home or Hospital has an individualised, up to date Care Plan.
- **Communication**:
    - Obtain a report from Person in charge and advise the Manager of any incident/accident and status of any residents/clients whose care/health is causing concern.
    - Supervise visits and liaise with GPs in order to establish a good relationship between the GPs/Health Care Professionals.

- Ensure kitchen personnel are aware of any special dietary needs. Supervise the serving of meals, ensuring that the special dietary needs of individual clients are being met.
- Liaise with relatives and discuss any matters relating to their family as necessary.
- Ensure a clear and concise handover report is given to all Staff Members.
- Participate in staff and residents/clients meetings and attend training sessions as required.

■ **Budgetary/financial control:**
- Be aware of the need to manage and maintain budgets agreed by the Manager and Head Office (if applicable).
- Ensure that all commodities used in and around the facility are sensibly conserved by all grades of staff, e.g. monitor usages of incontinence aids, wipes, dressings, electricity etc.

■ **Human resources:**
- Interview for new staff with the manager as and when required.
- Monitor and control sickness/absences/arrival/leave to avoid misuse.
- Continually assess and supervise the work of staff to ensure the maintenance of high standards of care, including creation of an atmosphere conducive to the best interests of the resident/client.
- Participate in the development, implementation and evaluation of appraisals and individual performance reviews as both employee and employer.

■ **Marketing:**
- Actively market the facility and promote a positive personal/professional profile within the local community, ensuring the good reputation of the Hospital at all times.

■ **Training and development:**
- Oversee induction process for new staff. Provide relevant medical/care related updates for staff. Provide guidance and assistance to all staff including active care process and report writing.

■ **Health and safety:**
- Report immediately to the Manager any illness of an infectious nature or accident incurred by a resident/client, colleague, self or another.
- Understand and ensure the implementation of the facilities Health and Safety Policy, Emergency and Fire Procedures.
- Report any faulty appliances, damaged furniture or equipment and any potential hazard to the Manager or in his/her absence to the maintenance person.

- **General**:
  - Promote and ensure the good reputation of the facility
  - Adhere to all appropriate NMC guidelines/regulations and policy/procedure laid down by the company.
  - Demonstrate non-discriminatory practice in all aspects of work.
  - Maintain and update/or keep current professional knowledge and competence.
  - Be 'on-call' for emergencies which may arise within the facility and to cover shifts if all other avenues have been exhausted.
  - Ensure that all information of a confidential nature gained in the course of work is not divulged to third parties.
  - Notify the Manager as soon as possible of the inability to report for duty, and also on the return to work from periods of absence.
  - Ensure the security of the facility is maintained at all times.
  - Adhere to all company policies and procedures within the defined timescales. Monitor and supervise practice within agreed company policies, procedures and protocols, NCSC standards and guidelines, Department of Health guidelines and legislation, including the Mental Health Act and Code of Practice.
  - Assist in the arrangements for charitable fund raising.
  - Take a lead role in the implementation of quality initiatives and audit, as defined in the Clinical Governance procedure.
  - Undertake other duties, as required, by the Manager.

Person specification

For new appointments, a selection panel will assess each of the points below against what you have written on the application form – so, as a job applicant, you should explain, by using examples from previous jobs, voluntary work or whilst you were in education, how you match these points.

To do this job effectively a person will need (essential criteria for this post are shown in bold):

- **Knowledge**
  - Fully conversant with the Mental Heath Act 1983
  - ENB 998 or equivalent Managerial Qualification/knowledge
  - A broad-based knowledge of current trends
  - Knowledge of local/national agendas with evidence of a comprehensive understanding of evidence of the impact these have on nursing practice and patient care
- **Skills**
  - Ability to communicate at all levels

- Team leader
- Ability to deputise in a management role
- Report writing skills
- Ability to maintain documentation and undertake audits
- Maintenance of staff rotas
- Ability to undertake in-house staff training
- Evidence of ability to network establish and maintain relationships with PCTs, local residents and representatives
- Good communicator, verbal and written
- Confident/assertive

■ **Qualifications**

At the time of appointment
- RMN (current PIN) or RGN (current PIN) in a care home setting
- Evidence of post-registration development
- Accredited Training/Courses
- Full driving licence (and willingness to drive)
- Relevant degree/diploma

Through professional development
Whilst in post and provided as organisational need and available resources dictate or, through self-funding if preferred by the post holder.
- Management qualifications

■ **Experience**:
- Minimum 18 months post registration or appropriate evidence of the same
- Evidence of functioning in a supervisory role as a clinician in a mental health/care home setting within a multi disciplinary team
- Experience of functioning/acting up as clinical lead
- Proven ability and experience to manage and resolve crisis and conflict within the workplace
- Evidence of developed skills in the assessment, planning, implementation and evaluation of multidisciplinary programmes of care for the client group
- Proven ability to lead set objectives and plan the development of staff within a staff team
- Evidence of leading a team within an independent care facility
- Previous supervisory/clinical lead experience

Having read this extensive job description and personal specification you may be able to recognise some of the areas that you may wish to concentrate on developing, in an endeavour to be successful in applying for a similar type of post, which in the future can often lead to further promotional opportunities.

It is acknowledged that we still need qualified practical clinical nurses who can deliver 'hands on' care in addition to our Heads of Care.

Business management and skills courses: useful website

The Open University: http://www.open.ac.uk/study/undergraduate/business-and-management/ (accessed 26 January 2010)

> Studying a business and management course with The Open University is all about you: Where you're at now and where you want to be in the future. Starting from your own experience, you will develop and extend your knowledge, skills and practice – whether you're looking for a one-off piece of professional updating or aiming for an award such as a Diploma or Business Degree.

NB: *It is important to note that many independent business management courses can be expensive and you should explore options by accessing the World Wide Web.*

Career development: the first staff nurse job

For newly registered nurses, the prospect of finding their first staff nurse position can seem like a daunting task.

I have noted, when listening to feedback in training sessions, that many newly registered nurses may feel that they need some level of guidance with regard to finding and securing their first staff nurses job.

After successfully completing their nurse training at university, newly registered nurses will often begin the search for a suitable staff nurse's post.

Some nursing students chose to move from the National Health Service (NHS) into the independent health care sector to take up their first staff nurse position. Care homes and independent hospitals can offer staff nurses a realistic career pathway, and have the potential to present many opportunities, for example becoming Head of Care or even a care home or hospital manager.

When applying for a staff nurse position, the NHS and large corporate care providers are now requiring staff to complete an online application form. It is important to be as accurate as you possibly can and not to try to embellish the online application form with information that is exaggerated and in some cases not factually correct.

Many employers like to arrange informal visits for candidates to tour the care home, and this is most useful to both parties. The employer can see the candidates and how they interact with the client group. An informal visit is also very useful to the candidate who can decide if they could work within the setting and the people that are already in post. First impressions really do make a difference at this stage in the recruitment process; therefore candidates should always try to create a professional and friendly impression if they want to be considered for short listing to interview.

However, some applicants may still be required to submit an up-to-date Curriculum Vitae (CV). The CV is a personal document of an individual's relevant qualifications, experience and skills that he or she is able to offer the prospective employer. It is also an opportunity to describe skills that, though not directly related to the role, may be transferable from a past experience, for example, prioritising duties or working within a team.

- When applying for a position, it is advisable, where possible, to read the job description and personal specification.
- The CV should be typed and be accompanied by a covering letter outlining the reasons for applying for the position.
- The CV should be interesting and succinct, including information about the individual and his or her skills. It is important to remember that the key aim is to provide prospective employers with a desire to request an interview.

Details that should be included in a CV

Your CV should include the following details:

- Personal details, including full name, address and telephone number
- Previous job history, including the key duties and the relevant skills that previous roles may have required
- Academic achievements in school and work (training programmes, certificates)
- Key achievements in school and/or college or previous positions
- Communication or any other special skills developed over the years

It is important to update a CV every six months to ensure that it contains the latest information, for example, completion of a course, new responsibilities or key achievements.

Your CV should include any personal information that you feel is specifically relevant to the post for which you are applying.

To convey your suitability for a job, it is very important to research the organisation in question. In doing so, it is likely that you will understand which of your personal traits and qualifications match with the staff nurse requirements.

By understanding this, and conveying this information in the CV and covering letter, your CV is more likely to catch the attention of a prospective employer, therefore increasing the likelihood of achieving an interview.

A common mistake is for people to draw up a general type of CV and only change the cover letter to send to the independent care companies. However, since each staff nurse's job is specific and has special requirements, it is reasonable to assume that one CV cannot match all of the jobs available throughout the NHS and the independent care sector.

There are several different views on the layout of a CV. There are many organisations that can be found on the Internet that offer advice on presenting information. One example of how to lay out a simple CV is detailed in Figure 1.1.

- The CV is an opportunity to 'sell you'. When including employment and education history it is important to list the dates of any training courses in addition to your nurse training.
- There should be no gaps in career history: any breaks should be accounted for (i.e. studying, travelling).
- The CV may be viewed against many other candidates, some of whom may have a lot more experience. However, a well crafted CV detailing experience, academic achievements, placements and transferable skills can help secure an interview.

The covering letter

The covering letter should form an important supplement to the CV to help the employer to understand why you are pursuing this particular post.

The letter must provide the reader with a brief overview. Remember that attention to detail is vital. A poorly written letter filled with spelling mistakes would create a poor impression of the writer searching for a new post.

It sounds simple, but it is important to include your home address, email address and a contact phone number.

Susan Ann Taylor
42 Barker Tree Walk
Melchester
M1 8PT

Email: susanataylor@AOL.com
Mobile Tel: 07779 800009

PIN XYXLXB9876

Employment History

Student Nurse   **Melchester University**
Senior Support Worker **Voluntary Services**
June 2002 to January 2004 Melchester Road, Stockton, WA15
I was responsible for managing the staff at Voluntary Services, a short breaks respite care centre for adults with severe learning disabilities and challenging behaviour. I was the team leader for the house and had over-all responsibility for the annual budget and the maintenance of the house. I achieved my NVQ Level 4 in Social Care in 2003.

Team Leader   **Fitzwarren Case Management**
March 2003 to June 2004   Fitzwarren House, Cheshire, WA1
                           2TT
I managed the development of a team of six care support workers employed by FCM to deliver 24-hour care for a young man with an acquired brain injury in his own home. I worked closely with the brain injury case manager to develop an individualised person-centred care plan.

Support worker   **Smithson Trust**
December 2002 to March 2003 Dell Close, Slesdale, CB3 7YH
I was responsible for two ladies with learning difficulties in their own homes. My duties included assisting them with budget planning, shopping and social activities.

Project worker   **Making it Charitable Trust**
April 2002 to December 2002 10 Smart Lane, Slesdale, CB3 9TG

Figure 1.1 An example of a Curriculum Vitae.

I worked with people who suffered from a variety of conditions including drug and alcohol abuse and mental health issues on two sites. With my support one of the people I worked closely with entered into the local community after spending years in social isolation. I studied for my NVQ level 2.

Support worker   **Wrentham Homes**
December 1995 to April 2002   19 Trench Close, Smithfield,
                    Cumbria
I worked with people who demonstrated challenging behaviour and who also had physical and mental disabilities in their own homes. I studied for my NVQ Levels 2 and 3 and I was also responsible for implementing a sensory activities programme during this interesting and rewarding time in my career.

Various positions working overseas
November 2000 to December 2001
I took one year out to tour the world including Thailand, Malaysia, Australia and New Zealand.

Educational/professional history

Qualification	Subject	Year
GCSE	7 passes	June 1983
NVQ Level 2	Special needs care	August 1998
NVQ Level 3	Business studies, Body massage	July 1999
	Basic First Aid, Health & Safety	April 2003
	Manual Handling, Basic Food	
	Hygiene	April 2003
NVQ Level 3	Social Care	February 2004

Activities/Interests
I am self-motivated and enjoy hard work and the various challenges that are associated with the care and support of adults with disabilities. I believe that after recently qualifying I will be able to make a real difference working as staff nurse and as part of a team at The Lodge Care Home.

I have no criminal convictions and possess a clean driving licence.

Figure 1.1 (continued)

Providing references

In many organisations, it is essential for professional references to be obtained from previous line managers covering the previous two or more years. However, to enable the employer to gain an all-round view, it is advisable to provide the details of additional referees who are happy to be contacted. The employer can then contact these people if they wish. These may be referees who perhaps tutored or supervised you but who were not your line manager. This can be useful for newly registered nurses; as such referees can highlight a candidate's potential and attitude.

These referees should not be related to the candidate as this will lead to a biased reference.

The interview process

It is quite normal to feel nerves before any job interview, and it is advisable to arrive at the care home or hospital a little early for an interview.

You should be dressed smartly in clothes in which you feel comfortable.

A staff nurse may be interviewed by the hospital manager and the Head of Care. The questions are usually standardised and will be the same for every candidate.

Questions should be answered as clearly as possible. If you are unsure of the meaning of the question you should ask the interviewer to clarify it. It is common for people to feel nervous, so interviewers are often asked to do this.

The main purpose of the interview is to try to demonstrate your suitability for the post. You should give examples of the work you have done both before and during your course. Many people are now taking up their training later on in life and can call upon their previous working experience.

Creating the right impression

An excellent way for candidates to convey enthusiasm for the post is to provide interviewers with evidence that they have some knowledge about the care home or hospital; this can be gained by visiting the website, reading a brochure about the services the care home or hospital provides, or speaking to friends and colleagues.

A PowerPoint presentation will give you the opportunity to demonstrate your ability to communicate your knowledge to the interview panel.

At the conclusion of the interview candidates are often offered a chance to ask any questions. It is important to ask some questions, as they demonstrate that you have thought seriously about your decision to apply for the post in the first place.

Body language

You will be at an advantage if you understand the importance of body language in an interview situation. Borg (2004) states:

> When we study body language and its effects, the most important thing to remember is that regardless of what a particular gesture means to you, it's how the receiver sees it that's important. Sitting perched on the edge of your seat creates a nervous impression. It can indicate to the other person that you don't want to be there.

Employers may have interviewed hundreds of people, and therefore have experience of putting nervous people at ease.

You should not be afraid to ask for a glass of water, for example, as this is infinitely better than sitting worrying about having a dry mouth.

Desirable qualities for a new staff nurse

A new staff nurse should be able to demonstrate clinical knowledge and an understanding of the area of nursing that you wish to specialise in.

A new staff nurse should be well motivated with genuine ambition and be able to demonstrate willingness to learn about the 'art of management'.

Managing staff in any care home setting can only be learned with 'hands-on experience' and newly appointed staff nurses will receive a period of induction followed by clinical supervision.

A new staff nurse will need a great deal of energy and enthusiasm as the hours are long and there is a great deal of new responsibility attached to the role.

Criminal Records Bureau (CRB)

The Criminal Records Bureau (CRB), an Executive Agency of the Home Office, provides wider access to criminal record information through its disclosure service. This service enables organisations in the public, private and voluntary sectors to make safer recruitment decisions by identifying candidates who may be unsuitable for certain work, especially that involving children or vulnerable adults.

The CRB was established under Part V of the Police Act 1997 and was launched in March 2002. Before 2002, access to police checks was mainly confined to organisations in the statutory sector for staff that had substantial unsupervised access to children. There were many other organisations that could not access these checks and yet had staff with similar access to vulnerable groups. The CRB check enables many more organisations to access these checks as part of good recruitment practice.

Organisations wishing to use the service can ask successful job applicants to apply for one of two types of check. Anyone working with vulnerable adults in a professional or voluntary capacity will be required to have completed a CRB and in some cases a POVA First check.

The Home Office web site provides clear guidance on the subject:

- For England these checks are described in Department of Health (DH) guidance on when a care worker may be allowed to start work in a care home, for a domiciliary care agency, or as an adult placement carer before a CRB check has been issued.
- In Wales, the provision only extends to care homes and nurses agency workers. Exceptions are permissible only where it is necessary to take such action because of a real danger that staffing levels will otherwise fall below the levels required to meet statutory obligations. The Commission for Social Care Inspection and the Care Standards Inspectorate for Wales will monitor applications for POVA First checks to ensure compliance with these criteria.

The CRB will aim to issue 98% of POVA First results within 48 hours and 100% within 72 hours (weekends and Bank Holidays are excluded).

The service standard starts only after the CRB has received a fully completed and valid disclosure application form and a valid POVA First request (http://www.crb.gov.uk/).

The type of check required will depend upon the nature of the position. The two types are called Enhanced and Standard Disclosures; both require a fee, but are free of charge to volunteers.

Therefore it is essential that all applicants for staff nurse posts and all types of other jobs involving caring for older people or young adults must be honest and disclose any criminal record. The employer will be forwarded a copy of the CRB/POVA First prior to the staff nurse commencing work The CRB checks are comprehensive and thankfully there is no hiding place for those who are trying to hide a criminal past. If a person is found to have lied in either their CV or application form then they could lose their job instantly.

Conclusion

Once a newly registered nurse has embarked on his or her first position, this could lead to the first step along the 'management journey'. The exciting thing about becoming a staff nurse is the realisation that the hard work has paid off with a nursing qualification. However, it is very important to remember that this is only the starting point of nursing career.

It is important for nurses to keep themselves up to date with current practice, and to attend regular courses and training sessions.

References

Ashurst, A. (2008) Career development: the first staff nurse job. *Nursing & Residential Care*, **10**(5), 253–6.

Borg, J. (2004) Persuasion – the art of influencing people. *Mind Your Body Language*. Pearson Education, Harlow.

Criminal Records Bureau: http://www.crb.homeoffice.gov.uk/; accessed 26 January 2010.

Key points

- It is always advisable to read the staff nurse's job description and the personal specification before completing a CV.
- The CV is an opportunity to 'sell yourself'.
- The covering letter should form an important supplement to the CV and help the employer understand an applicant's suitability for a position.
- The Criminal Records Bureau (CRB), an Executive Agency of the Home Office, provides wider access to criminal record information through its disclosure service.

Your current position

You may be a newly registered nurse just about to embark on your first staff nurses position within the independent health care sector or you may be currently working in an Head of Care or a Unit Manager's role, being employed by a large company and seeking promotion to a Care Home Manager's position.

If you are already in a management position then you may be looking to progress into a regional/operations management post with a large care provider. However, it is important to note that in some cases care providers have recently changed their emphasis in the make-up of the management structure. Several new management positions have been created, such as Quality Assurance and Compliance managers and business managers.

Some registered nurses may choose to become clinical specialists and nurse consultants who play an important role in the development of local and national clinical nursing strategy.

Wherever you see yourself in the future, you must try to devise a simple action plan as to how you are going to achieve your goals. It is important to recognise the enormous workload that is now associated with the Care Home Manager's role.

You should always take full advantage of the supervision process and discuss your personal goals with your mentor and manager.

Discussion points

■ Why is it important to take an active role in the supervision process?
■ Why do you think care providers have introduced Quality Assurance and Compliance managers and business managers?
■ Discuss the reasons why you are seeking promotion with your line manager.

CHAPTER 2

Developing your management skills

Is your management up to scratch?

Having spent the last 15 years working in the independent healthcare sector in senior management positions, I recognise that staffs today have a certain expectation: that their senior managers will treat them with respect and a sense of fairness.

Employers within the independent health-care sector as a whole must be mindful of the serious consequences that poor management styles have within their organisations and the effect that this behaviour has on staff morale.

Senior managers are very well paid to provide stakeholders with a return on the investment made to build successful businesses.

The ruthlessness of multimillionaire businessman Sir Alan Sugar (now Lord Sugar) was plain for all to see in the excellent reality television series *The Apprentice*, transmitted on BBC2. Is this style of autocratic management the way forward for the healthcare industry?

We must never forget that the aim of our business is to care for others less fortunate than ourselves.

Healthcare companies need to make money in order to maintain high standards of service and also meet the expectations of service users in a very competitive market. Many leading care providers are spending millions of pounds each year developing their care homes by acquisition and refurbishment. Nevertheless, it is possible that the independent healthcare sector may lose some of its most talented staff and junior managers because of the constant drive to meet care home occupancy expectations.

- Senior managers today are in many cases under enormous stress at work and they are working well over the 48 hours a week as described in the European Working Time Directive (Department of Health, 2009).

What is the European Working Time Directive?

The EWTD is a directive from the Council of Europe (93/104/EC) to protect the health and safety of workers in the European Union. It lays down minimum requirements in relation to working hours, rest periods, annual leave and working arrangements for night workers.

The Directive was enacted into UK law as the Working Time Regulations, which took effect from October 1998. The Government negotiated an extension of up to twelve years to prepare for full implementation for doctors in training.

The legal definition of working time

> Working time shall mean any period during which the worker is working, at the employer's disposal and carrying out his or her activity or duties, in accordance with national laws and/or practice.

Stress and workload

The stress often experienced by senior managers is compounded when their families face the prospect of their partners having to answer work-related emails well into most evenings of the week and at the weekends, just to keep up to speed with their workload.

Whatever happened to the theory of the need for a decent balance between work and family life?

Take a look at your own organisation today and ask yourself the following questions:

- Does your immediate line manager appear happy in his or her work?
- How many line managers have you had in the last 12 months?
- Do you know why people are leaving the company?
- Are you happy with the amount of unpaid overtime you have to do every week?
- What is your company doing about stress-related illnesses within your care home?

The consequences of poor management styles can destroy businesses overnight. Bullying, pressure and fear should have no place in the caring profession.

People should be paid well and valued for doing their best in the roles for which they have been appointed.

There are some brilliant employers in the independent healthcare sector and they are able to demonstrate their success in the way they successfully manage, train and retain their staff.

References

Ashurst, A. (2005) Is your management up to scratch? *Nursing & Residential Care*, **7**(7), 289.

Department of Health (2009) http//www.dh.gov.uk/; accessed 23 December 2009.

Key points

- Employers within the independent healthcare sector as a whole must be mindful of the serious consequences that poor management styles have within their organisations and the effect that this behaviour has on staff morale.
- 'Working time shall mean any period during which the worker is working, at the employer's disposal and carrying out his or her activity or duties, in accordance with national laws and/or practice.'
- The consequences of poor management styles can destroy businesses overnight. Bullying, pressure and fear should have no place in the caring profession.

Discussion points

- Is Lord Alan Sugar's autocratic management style suited to the independent healthcare sector?
- What is your company doing about stress-related illnesses within your care home?
- What do you think is the most effective management style to be used in a care home today?

Budgets – a simple guide

Mason (2007) states:

A budget is a plan expressed in financial terms.

Budgets enable, or perhaps force, managers to plan ahead logically and constructively. This means considering such things as:

- Where do we intend to be at the end of the budget period?
- How a department and budget interact with other departments and other budgets.
- Are there any limiting factors and what are they?
- What actions must be taken to achieve budgeted results?
- What are the realistic, achievable targets to set ourselves?

Family budget

You may be thinking of planning a family summer holiday and the first thing you must do is to discuss how much your family can afford to spend on your holiday of a lifetime, even during these difficult economic times.

Many people search the Internet to help them find the best 'value for money' offers.

Another option is to search the brochures from a local travel agent after discussing your requirements with the holiday experts 'face to face'.

You have already budgeted for the day-to-day requirements of the family, including the monthly mortgage repayments, credit card repayments, loan repayments, car expenses, council taxes, savings, pension payments, house maintenance, clothes, food, buildings and contents insurance etc.

The most important part of your family budget may only balance if both adults are working and in secure employment. The danger of budgeting is that we take things for granted in our lives. Imagine if one person in the relationship suddenly loses their job; the original budget is at serious risk of being exceeded.

The family may even end up holidaying in the United Kingdom rather than the two weeks of luxury in the Caribbean. People may choose to put the holiday on the credit card, but this has serious financial consequences and may result in personal debts for many years to come.

The family budget is something you manage as an integral part of you lives. In reality, the family budget is similar in many ways to the business budget.

Business budgets

Years ago, many care home managers were never involved in the complexity of the budget process. They simply had responsibility for the clinical care of the residents.

The care home owner usually kept all financial matters 'close to the chest'. Care home managers had to trust their employers to provide anything that they requested. Sadly this often led to frustration as the sole proprietor care home owners did not have massive cash reserves.

A care home's success was based upon full occupancy, developing a good reputation and ensuring that residents, social services and the resident's families all paid their fees on time.

However, over time in the United Kingdom large corporate care providers developed large care homes with up to 120 beds, and even integrated care villages have emerged in improving facilities to care for older people.

Today care home managers are usually involved in the budget and business planning process. Therefore they must be able to understand what impact the budget they agree with their employers is going to have on their care home's overall performance over the following twelve months.

Where do we intend to be at the end of the budget period?

The year is divided into four quarters and managers receive a set of detailed accounts every month to give a clear indication as to the progress of the care home against the annual budget forecast. From the accounts it is easy to see which departments are over-spending and which areas are doing well and staying within budget.

At the end of each financial year the target is to be in profit, with the staff providing a high standard of care in an environment that everyone is proud to be associated with.

How a department and budget interact with other departments and other budgets

As the care home manager, it is vital that you have an understanding of how each of the departments spend its budget. For example, are the chefs getting 'value for money' from their local suppliers? How much money is being spent on staff each month and is this in line with the budget?

Are there any limiting factors and what are they?

One of the most important aspects of running a successful care home is to ensure that the occupancy is maintained throughout the year. Unfortunately there are some times when occupancy drops – it may be that a new care home opens in close proximity to your care facility.

Reputations can take years to develop, but one serious incident that leads to local poor publicity in the media or a poor CQC inspection report may result in a dip in referrals.

The secret of success is for the care home manager to anticipate difficulties and have a contingency plan. What is your care home's unique selling point? Care homes in danger of failing must be flexible and willing to diversify into caring for different residents in order to meet their budget expectations.

What actions must be taken to achieve budgeted results?

As a care home manager you may be called upon to make some difficult and unpopular decisions. Meeting the budget forecast every month is very important as it is difficult to make up in the year if you are spending more than you are taking in from fees. You may have to reduce spending in areas and ensure that everyone takes personal responsibility for their spending.

You may have to consider recommending to the care home owner that you introduce a new resident's fee increase or suggest taking in a number of more difficult and challenging residents to fill the empty beds. Any change of use in the care home must be fully discussed, but it may be the key to your care home's survival.

What are the realistic, achievable targets to set ourselves?

As a care home manager it is not advisable to agree to a budget forecast that you know you can never hope to achieve. Instead, negotiate a deal that provides you with a realistic chance of success. Many care home managers have annual bonuses based on the care home's financial performance.

Capital expenditure

Mason (2007) suggests that:

It should be remembered that capital expenditure is the purchase of items that have a value to the business in the long term. This is opposed to revenue expenditure which is short term.

Capital expenditure is divided into categories such as freehold property, leasehold property, plant and machinery, fixtures and fittings, computers and motor vehicles.

This budget is usually controlled and managed at Director level, and therefore the care home manager needs to identify what is required at the beginning of the budget planning process.

References

Mason, R. (2007) *Finance for Non-financial Managers*. Hodder Education, London.

Time management

Care home managers and registered nurses should endeavour to develop methods of coping with time constraints that are forced upon them, not only in their working environment but in their home lives too. Achieving a satisfactory work–life balance requires a personal strategy. This can be achieved by nurses recognising where their priorities actually lie.

Family are essential to maintaining well-being and personal relationships can be tested to breaking point as commitment to work takes over your life.

Time management has been defined as being a:

Systematic, priority-based structuring of time allocation and distribution among competing demands. Since time cannot be stored and its availability can neither be increased beyond nor decreased from the 24-hours, the term 'time budgeting' is said to be the more appropriate one (Business Dictionary, 2008)

It is important therefore that nurses wishing to achieve a true work–life balance recognise and adopt some practical methods to achieve a more fulfilling lifestyle.

There are 168 hours in every week. The average working week is 37½ hours, but anecdotal evidence suggests that nurses and managers often work many hours overtime and this may include frequent 'on-call' responsibilities.

Table 2.1 Finding more time (adapted from Ashton (2004)).

- Make a list – at the end of each day, list in order of priority things you must do tomorrow. Listing it now gets your morning off to a flying start.

- Have treats – we are all human, so working flat out will not produce the best results. (Ensure that you have some special social event to attend. If you do not have a social life then there may be a danger that you become trapped in an 'all work and no play' scenario).

- Check reality – do not budget to fill every working hour. At least 20% of your time will be spent doing administration, sorting out queries and troubleshooting. (As a newly registered nurse, you will also need to assist in care planning, writing clinical reports and provide hands-on care for your residents.)

Ashton (2004) suggests: 'It's all too easy to fill your diary with things to do, people to meet and deadlines to hit. Here are some ways to make more of each day'.

Table 2.1 provides ideas for finding more time.

Time management approaches

Managing time more effectively is each person's personal responsibility. However, care home managers can offer support in finding ways to do this.

A systematic approach

Some of the most successful business men and women appear to be able to take on many tasks at the same time. The secret of their success appears to be in the implementation of a systematic approach.

For nurse practitioners, there is a simple formula designed to determine an individual time management action plan.

Managing your priority list

It is one thing to write out a to-do list of tasks but quite another one to manage it effectively. To get the most out of a list, follow these instructions by Hoover (2007) it may help to:

- Arrange tasks in order of importance and urgency.
- Re-write the list as priorities change or circumstances change.
- Tackle the list by completing the first item on it, then moving onto the next one systematically.
- Clean up and re-write the list every day (before you leave the care home).
- Take an upbeat attitude towards the tasks so that each one seems worthy of your time.

Ashurst (2006) provides the interesting example of newspaper journalists and photographers working on a daily newspaper:

- These committed staff members appear to thrive on meeting strict deadlines on a daily basis.
- They are able to produce interesting stories and pictures every day, which are read by thousands of people over breakfast or whilst travelling on the train/bus on their way to work the following day.
- Failure to meet these strict and immovable deadlines would result in much smaller newspapers, with less news items and advertising.
- Eventually, these failing newspapers would go out of business very quickly.

Reviewing your communication skills

At the end of the day shift, it is important to provide a detailed verbal and written handover to the care home night staff. There are many other duties, not mentioned in this list that may have to be carried out daily.

Job satisfaction

Nursing often provides nurses with great job satisfaction. However, it must be recognised that, at times, the job can be both physically and mentally exhausting.

Taking holidays and time off are very important if staff are to remain motivated and focused. We all need the time to re-charge our batteries, and newly qualified staff need to recognise that their days off are to be taken for a reason. However, in some emergencies, most staff are often willing to come into the care home and cover for sickness. It is always important to remember that holiday not taken by your staff at the beginning of the year only results in it accumulating, and there can be a serious backlog of outstanding holidays later in the year.

Table 2.2 Setting SMART objectives (adapted from Ashurst (2008, p. 356)).

- **Specific**: identifies that objectives are written clearly, describing exactly what every staff needs to do in order to achieve excellent clinical results.

- **Measurable**: objectives that provide staff with recognised clinical standards that can be achieved and exceeded with the resources provided.

- **Achievable**: objectives should always be achievable. It is frustrating for staff to be set targets which they cannot achieve; they can become demotivated as a result.

- **Realistic**: the objectives must be written in a manner that recognises actual time restraints and there must be evidence that appropriate staff training and development is in place.

- **Timely**: agreed objectives must be met within a set time frame agreed with the care provider and the individual inspectorate body.

Caunt (2000) suggests that in order to implement a method of planning and tracking your time, you need to be able to:

Determine your objectives; break assignments down into their component tasks and identify what you will need from others, in order that you can complete your own tasks.

The care home manager is responsible for setting the overall objectives. Nurses are responsible for implementing these objectives, which should follow the **SMART** specification (Table 2.2).

Daily deadlines

Newly registered nurses working in care homes and independent hospitals are expected to meet daily deadlines. Examples of things that may need to be carried out in a care home every day are listed below:

- On day duty, the staff must attend the handover on time from the night staff. This provides a factual update on each resident.
- Punctuality is really important; if people wander in late for the briefing then they will have to be told the information second hand from other staff.
- The Head of Care or Unit Manager will have to ensure that all staff are given their individual daily allocation of duties; residents and patients need

to be woken and provided with breakfast and then bathed at some time during the day.

- Team members are encouraged to respect the residents' wishes and not insist that a resident bathes or showers at a certain time.
- The residents must receive their medication on time and this must be administered and recorded in the appropriate and professional manner.
- Meal times for residents are very time-consuming and must be planned in conjunction with the head chef.
- Appropriate activities and outings should be arranged in conjunction with the residents at the residents' forum.
- Nurses and carers should be encouraged to make time to talk with residents and their relatives. This time spent communicating with residents and relatives will be well spent if, in the future, they raise any concerns about their care in the care home.
- By using their time effectively, nurses will have developed a professional working relationship between the resident, relatives and themselves, rather than just acting as strangers.
- Clinical review meetings and multidisciplinary team meetings need to be organised to discuss the residents' care plans.
- In addition, nurses are often expected to write detailed nursing reports on the residents as well as completing residents' up-to-date reports daily. These reports may be written in the evenings.
- Team members are expected to attend regular staff meetings.
- Meetings can be very time-consuming and it is therefore useful to set a time limit and always produce an agenda that must be followed.
- Staff training and development are important and time should be carefully planned to ensure not only that that staff receive induction and mandatory training, but that they are encouraged to undertake further study.
- Supervision and appraisal meetings are a vital means of providing staff with feedback on their progress. Time must be set aside for these meetings, bearing in mind the service needs of the residents.
- Time cannot be controlled; therefore you must learn to organise, delegate and accept personal responsibility for making the time to create an effective and efficient care team.

Attention to detail concerning the care home environment can make a real difference to the residents' quality of life. A planned re-decorating programme ensures that the care home always appears clean and fresh.

Finally, we must also appreciate that we ourselves need to take time out and relax with our families and friends in a social setting. For once, why not arrange for someone else to do the on-call duty? Some managers find themselves having to work many hours overtime as their staff are unable to find time to complete the many aspects of completing their resident/patient documentation.

Conclusion

For newly registered nurses, managing their time effectively can take a lot of practice. There will be days or nights when all that is set out to deal with is not achieved. Emergencies and unforeseen circumstances can occur at any time.

The residents' care must always remain the first priority, with individual and colleagues' well-being a close second.

Without motivated and happy staff, morale within the care home can decline and sickness absence levels rise very quickly. Some team members may decide to leave and seek other employment. This in turn could lead to a higher than usual use of agency staff, which can cause residents and their relatives to become unhappy because there appears to be a lack of continuity in care.

It is difficult to recruit staff to a care home in decline. As a result, occupancy may go down and this may eventually result in the care home's sale or closure. To avoid this scenario, the care home manager and registered nurses need to recognise the importance of practising good time management and valuing their staff's off-duty time.

References

Ashton, R. (2004) *The Entrepreneur's Book of Checklists*, p. 72. Pearson Education, Harlow.

Ashurst, A. (2006) *Managing a Care Home*. Quay Books, London.

Ashurst, A. (2008) Career development: time management. *Nursing & Residential Care*, **10**(7), 354–6.

Business Dictionary. http://www.businessdictionary.com/. Accessed 6 June 2008.

Caunt, J. (2000) *Organise Yourself*. Kogan Page. London.

Hoover, J. (2007) *Time Management – Set Priorities to Get Things Done*, p. 30. Hylas Publishing, Irvington, New York.

Key points

■ Care home managers and registered nurses should endeavour to develop methods within the time constraints that are forced upon them, not only in their working environment but in their home lives.

- It's all too easy to fill your diary with things to do, people to meet and deadlines to hit.
- Meal times for residents are very time-consuming and must be planned in conjunction with the head chef.
- Time cannot be controlled but we must learn to organise, delegate and accept personal responsibility for making the time to create a staff team and environment that makes a real difference to the residents' quality of life.

Discussion points

- How do you manage your work time?
- Write a priority list for your staff team – always appreciate that key nurses and key support workers do have named residents/patients to care for.
- Discuss with your team different ways to improve everyone's time management.
- Remember to keep your meetings as brief as possible. Deal with the most important items on the agenda first.
- Set aside time each week to review residents' care plans.
- Arrange times for relatives to meet with you to discuss any issues they may be concerned about.

Management styles explained

Autocratic

An autocratic or authoritarian manager makes all the decisions, keeping the information and decision making among the senior management team. In a care home setting this can be very disruptive as the registered nurses and care support staffs need to be kept informed about the clinical needs of their residents on a day-to-day basis.

Objectives and tasks are set by the care home manager and the team members are expected to do exactly as required.

The communication involved with this method is mainly downward, from the care home manager to the staff.

Staff can sometimes become disillusioned when being kept in the dark about decisions affecting their work.

The main advantages of this management style are that the direction of the business will remain constant and the decisions will all be similar. This in turn can project the image of a confident, well-managed care home business.

On the other hand, staff may become dependent upon the care home manager.

From the autocratic manager's perspective they may have been let down in the past by staff and feel the need to keep a tight rein on the care home's budget and staff working practices

Paternalistic

A more paternalistic manager is also essentially dictatorial; however, the decisions tend to be in the best interests of the staff rather than the care business. A good example of this would be the fictional David Brent running the business in the television show *The Office*.

The leader explains most decisions to the employees and ensures that their social and leisure needs are always met. This can help balance out the lack of staff motivation caused by an autocratic management style.

Feedback from the manager is again generally downward; however, feedback to the management team will occur in order for the staff team to be kept happy.

This style can be highly advantageous, and can engender loyalty from the staff, leading to lower staff turnover thanks to the emphasis on their social needs. It shares similar disadvantages with an authoritarian style: employees become dependent on the leader, and if the wrong decisions are made then all employees may become dissatisfied with the leader.

Democratic

In a democratic style, the care home manager allows the staff to take part in decision-making: therefore everything is agreed by the majority. The communication is extensive in both directions (from staff to managers and vice versa). This style can be particularly useful when complex decisions need to be made that require a range of specialist skills: for example, when a new IT system needs to be put in place and the upper management of the business is computer-illiterate.

From the overall care home's point of view, job satisfaction and quality of work will improve. However, the decision-making process is severely slowed down, and the need for a consensus may prevent the 'best' decision for the company being taken.

Laissez-faire

In a *laissez-faire* management style, the leader's role is peripheral and staff tend to manage their own areas of the care home; the manager therefore evades the duties of management and uncoordinated delegation occurs. The communication in this style is horizontal, meaning that it is equal in both directions. However, very little communication occurs in comparison with other styles. The style brings out the best in highly professional and creative groups of employees, but in many cases this is not deliberate and is simply a result of poor management. This leads to a lack of staff focus and sense of direction, which in turn leads to much dissatisfaction and a poor company image.

Reference

Adapted from: http://www.answers.com/topic/management-styles; accessed 10 October 2009.

Key points

- An autocratic or authoritarian manager makes all the decisions, keeping the information and decision making among the senior management team.
- A more paternalistic manager is also essentially dictatorial; however, the decisions tend to be in the best interests of the staff rather than the care business.
- In a democratic style, the care home manager allows the staff to take part in decision-making: therefore everything is agreed by the majority.
- In a *laissez faire* management style, the leader's role is peripheral and staff tend to manage their own areas of the care home.

Discussion points

- Which management style do you normally have?
- Do you ever change your management style?
- Which management style suits you and your team best?

CHAPTER 3

Improving your communications

Improving your communications – Part 1

In order to make a real difference, managers and staff need to make a personal commitment to their customers. It is worth remembering that we are all customers – we should be prepared to treat others as we would like to be treated ourselves.

...

What did you do today to make you feel proud?

So sang Heather Small in her inspirational pop ballad of 2000. The song was once used by a care provider I worked for to be their motivational theme tune throughout the company's annual managers and staff conference.

Every morning, when the delegates arrived for the conference, we were greeted by the song, almost as a rallying call. At the end of the two-day conference, we all knew every single word and I couldn't get the tune out of my head for weeks.

The one thing the repeated playing of the song did was to make me, as a regional manager, stop and think about what practical steps I could take to make a real difference for managers, staff and residents every day.

Motivating your managers and staff can make a real difference to the way they deliver their customer service.

Watching Premiership football managers in action can give a clear insight into the art of inspirational management techniques. When your team is winning, the atmosphere throughout the club is positive and upbeat. Then look at some of the teams struggling to avoid relegation. The players' lack confidence and direction, and seem to miss open goals almost every week.

Likewise, some NHS wards, departments and independent care homes suffer from poor leadership and ineffective managers. If poor leadership is allowed to go unchecked, staff can become demoralised and lack confidence and direction. A combination of management issues can quickly result in poor care standards. Sickness and absence levels rise and the turnover of staff and managers follows. Complaints rise and morale plummets.

One of the major requirements for Primary Care Trusts (PCTs) is to receive information on a regular basis that is appropriate, timely and relevant to identify the successes made.

Care programme approach reviews remain the main interface between the funders and the multidisciplinary team members. We are refining our systems and have gained feedback from the PCT and community care coordinators, which allows us to improve and exceed our customers' expectations.

In order to make a real difference, managers and staff need to make a personal commitment to their customers. It is worth remembering that we are all customers – we should be prepared to treat others as we would like to be treated ourselves.

Ask yourself at the end of every shift: 'What did I do today to make me feel proud?'.

Reflecting on your practice will, I am sure, make a real difference not only to you but also to your patients and colleagues.

Reference:

Ashurst, A. (2007) On making a real difference. *Health Service Journal*.

Career progression: improving your communications – Part 2

Essential ingredients

Good communication is one of the essential ingredients of developing an effective and efficient care home staff team. Many aspects of the working environment require good communication skills: from answering the telephone to talking to the relatives of residents. The newly registered nurse practitioner (staff nurse) must be able to communicate effectively with professional colleagues, residents, relatives and visitors to the care home on a daily basis.

Active listening

Working in a care home requires all staff members to listen to each other. How well staff listen to their colleagues often affects what action they take. Sometimes we only hear what we want to hear, and as a result we may assume what has been said. This is an important concept for your staff to understand, especially at daily handover meetings, when day and night staff get together to discuss the care of the residents.

Plant (1987) suggests active listening to be:

A difficult concept to get across in words but is more than not talking.

It means not only hearing the messages but working hard to clarify and make sense of them:

Without doubt the key to active listening – and good quality general management – is the ability to ask good questions without presuming to answer them yourself. Try it at home one evening. Ask why, how, when, where, what, just nod your head and encourage and, above all, keep your mouth shut and eyes and ears open. You might be surprised just how much you learn. Then try it at work (Plant, 1987).

Nurse practitioners working in a busy care home environment need to recognise that they are part of the management team and that listening skills must be worked on and developed if they are to become effective managers.

Caring for older people, many of whom may be suffering from dementia, requires a great deal of patience, and the ability to listen to residents' fears, hopes and aspirations remains extremely important in making people feel that they are actually valued; that what they are saying is listened to and acted upon. It is also very important that nurses and carers listen to the relatives and friends of the older residents.

Recognising your residents' needs

This is particularly instrumental in helping to develop an understanding of the resident and his or her holistic needs and also those of the family. Residents' expectations of all aspects of their stay in a care home have increased dramatically over the last decade. It is important to allow residents and their relatives to put their opinions, their requirements and their expectations forward without fear of being judged.

Residents' and relatives' forums are one method of communicating people's feelings and views about the care home. However, it may be more effective to carry out confidential residents and relatives surveys.

Feedback

If a resident or family's requests may not be achievable in the short-term, then active listening can be conveyed by providing regular feedback and keeping people informed. Successful care homes are those that engage well with their residents and relatives.

This method of communicating with residents and relatives is not just exclusive to nurses and carers, but involves all staff, including those working in the care home's reception, administration department, kitchen, maintenance and housekeeping personnel.

Managers should not be afraid of canvassing their staff's views in regular confidential employees' surveys.

This reflective method of listening is now implemented effectively and considered the 'norm' among some of the countries leading corporate care providers. By developing listening and feedback skills, all those working in the care home can dramatically improve the standard of care and service they deliver to their residents. This in turn is likely to affect staff morale positively.

In the author's experience of managing people in care home settings, staff team members often feel valued when they are listened to. Likewise, residents and relatives are often pleased and satisfied when their 'customer expectations' are exceeded by receiving a level of care and a care environment that reminds them positively of their own home.

Francis and Young (1979) suggest:

Active listening shows that you respect and value their contribution. It may be difficult to accept the idea but the differences between people offer a resource for progress. But if you manage to bridge the differences, there is much of value to be gained.

Table 3.1 Techniques that can help listening (source: Francis and Young, 1979).

- **Checking**: 'Can I repeat what you said in order to check my understanding?'
- **Clarifying**: 'It seems to me to mean...'
- **Showing support**: 'I hear you, please carry on...'
- **Building on**: 'Building on your last point, I would add...'

Table 3.1 lists some of the techniques which can be useful in developing your listening skills.

Barriers to good communication

Sensory impairments

Many older people living in care experience diminished sight and hearing, which naturally makes communicating more difficult. Help is available from RNID and RNIB in terms of facilitating caring environments for those with sensory loss.

To aid communication with residents with sensory impairment, it is useful to work closely with the resident and their families to learn how they communicate with each other at home.

Libraries can offer 'talking books' and both the RNID and RNIB also offer valuable advice on communicating more effectively with these residents.

RNID and RNIB: further information

The Royal National Institute for Deaf People
19–23 Featherstone Street
London
EC1Y 8SL
http://www.rnid.org.uk/

The Royal National Institute of Blind People
105 Judd Street
London
WC1H 9NE
http://www.rnib.org.uk/

Language difficulties

Many care homes employ staff who were originally from overseas countries and there may be some instances of staff having difficulties in understanding what residents may say and vice versa. A local accent used by care home staff may also lead to some confusion among overseas staff. It is important that these issues are addressed in staff meetings and residents' and relatives' forums.

Trouble being heard

Working as a member of a care team, staff may find themselves in some difficulties if the care team is poorly managed and there is a low level of listening to each other.

Francis and Young (1979) suggest that those teams that have a low level of listening will show the following characteristics:

- Dominance by a few members
- Cross-talk (several members talking at once)
- Ideas lost (no mechanisms for catching and retaining points)
- Repetitive contributions
- Wordy inputs (individuals use much speaking time for little content)
- Inability to handle consensus decision making

On the other hand, a team that sets a high standard of listening skills is usually a pleasure to work in. As it communicates much more effectively and not as many things are missed concerning important messages. The group as a whole is much more cohesive and there is a consistent approach to care and service delivery. Individuals often display a high level of commitment to each other, demonstrating greater flexibility and support for fellow colleagues than the less successful team.

Improving staff attitudes

Care staff who are resistant to change may, on occasion, be very difficult to motivate and manage on a daily basis. However, it is important to recognise and acknowledge any reasons for their personal dissatisfaction at work.

Newly registered nurses may often lack the experience to give instructions to more experienced care staff. Some may also feel intimidated by the fact that staff may have been in post for many years.

One method of improving staff attitudes in a busy care home is to ensure that all staff have access and the opportunity to receive regular supervision and appraisal.

Supervision

In supervision sessions, team members have the opportunity to air their feelings about their role and progress within it. These important supervision sessions may be held on a one-to-one basis or within a small group.

The principles of good supervision are designed to provide employees with the opportunity to meet and discuss their progress with their line manager and work together with a Registered nurse to agree an action plan to improve their work performance and satisfaction. One of the key components of successful supervision is to recognise a person's specific relevant training needs. However, staff must be given the adequate time to undertake approved training courses that have been identified by their line manager as being necessary to improve their ability to carrying out their duties to the best of their ability.

Verbal communication

Leading a shift in a care home means that the registered nurse has to earn the respect of his or her colleagues and, with the care home manager's support, the newly registered nurse will begin to gain experience in this important aspect of his or her role.

Good role models are is knowledgeable and willing to explain clearly the answers to the many questions raised by junior staff, and they must be prepared to work 'hands on' with other team members.

After the daily handover meeting, the nurse in charge will allocate duties to the staff on duty. The manner in which he or she passes information on to the team is vital in ensuring that everyone understands what is expected of them.

This information-giving procedure can be successfully facilitated by ensuring that instructions are clear, concise and easy to understand.

- Verbal instructions should be reinforced by written records and using effective resident care plans that are regularly evaluated and updated to reinforce the message.
- Guidance and leadership that are given to staff should be consistent and not changed.

Case study: a sporting example

Staff do require a solid structure to work within, and if people change the way things are done serious mistakes can be made.

Imagine being part of a football or hockey team with a coach that changed his or her mind after every game.

The tactics and personnel are changed and you have a week to learn the new approach to the next game. It comes as no surprise to you or your team mates and the few fans you have left when you lose again, and so the depressing run of matches without a win goes on.

The team would begin to lose any confidence it had gained when it was actually winning games.

The reason that is usually given is that the team manager has lost the dressing room, and despite the chairman's praise, the manager is very quickly looking for another job.

The same rules apply to your care team.

They rely heavily on the manager and the head of care to speak with one voice, and both staff morale and the residents' standards of care will improve if the care home manager and all the staff are consistent and singing from the same hymn sheet each and every day.

I believe that management is not rocket science but you need to be able to recognise quickly when things are going wrong and have the confidence to stop, re-think and start again.

Managers can only really know what is happening in the care home if they are prepared to get out of their office and on to the floor every day, actively talking to their staff and residents, to ensure that staff are providing the high standards of care expected in a warm and friendly environment.

Those managers who fail to walk the floor may very quickly lose the care team's respect and ultimately their jobs.

Never assume that all is well, as people will always tell you there are no problems. There are usually issues in the care home which will only surface when they have become very difficult to resolve.

Improving daily reports

Poor daily reports with little or no information about the resident's activities during the day and how they have actually slept at night provide no evidence of what type of care the person is receiving.

Daily reports need to be delivered without the nurses using jargon.

Information needs to be factual and timely. There can be serious consequences if nurses fail to report information regarding the state of a resident's physical and mental health.

Policies and procedures

Staff nurses have an obligation to read and implement the care home's policies and procedures, which must then be shared with other staff. It is therefore
important that the policies and procedures are written in a clear and concise
manner. As an integral part of all newly appointed staff induction programmes,
the policies and procedures must be read and staff should sign to state that they
have read the documents and understood the contents.

Developing skills

To develop the necessary skills to improve communications, staff need to
recognise the principles of good verbal and written communication. A newly
registered nurse may feel overwhelmed when he or she has to attend the first
meeting with the rest of the care home team. However, confidence will grow
with experience.

It is important to remember that residents' records are legal documents.
Griffith (2007) explains that:

> The main purpose of keeping records is to have an account of the care
> and treatment given to a patient. This allows progress to be monitored
> and a clinical history to be developed. The clinical record allows for
> continuity of care by facilitating treatment and support.

Residents' care plans must therefore be written in a manner that can impart
instructions to other staff, explaining simply how residents should be cared for,
treated and supported.

If there is a lack of consistency staff may become confused, and this can
lead to dissatisfaction amongst some of the team members. Regular face-to-
face meetings with residents and their relatives can often defuse potential
problems and the staff nurse who gets to know his or her residents as their
named nurse can produce benefits. His or her knowledge of the resident and
the family means that holistic care, including meeting the residents' social,
spiritual, physical and psychological needs, can be provided.

Non-verbal communications

Stephenson (2008) states:

Non-verbal communication refers to body language, for example: facial expressions, eye contact and posture. Observing non-verbal behaviour can reveal a great deal of information about your patient or client. However, it can also send mixed messages, for example: a patient or client may say they are fine but have a worried expression and not be able to keep eye contact, which could indicate the opposite of what they are saying.

It is important for staff to appreciate that new residents have many issues that they may be unable to share when they are first admitted to the care home. It is therefore important for staff to spend time ensuring that trusting professional relationships are built.

Answering the telephone

How staff answer the telephone provides members of the public and potential customers with their first impression of the care home. It therefore follows that to maintain a high standard of customer service all staff need to learn the correct telephone answering protocol, which will be individual to every care home.

Golden rules for answering the telephone

1. Always answer the phone in a standardised manner with the name of the establishment and your name.
2. Ensure that if you cannot connect the caller to the person they wish to speak to then take the callers number and pass on the written telephone message.
3. It is good practice to record all received phone calls with the callers name and time of the call.

Written communications:

Nurses today are expected to spend a great deal of their time writing daily records on the activities and care delivered to their residents. All records should be written concisely, factually and free of bias. It is crucial to use good gram-

Answering the phone correctly is vital in the quest to deliver excellent customer care.

mar and accurate spelling, as if something is not written down it may never have happened.

Written communications are very important and must always be recognised as legal documents; they must therefore be stored safely. Good communications between staff, residents and relatives are essential if the care home is to succeed in exceeding people's expectations.

References

Ashurst, A. (2008) Career progression: improving communication. *Nursing & Residential Care*, **10**(8), 406–8.

Francis, D. and Young, D. (1979) *Improving Work Groups – A Practical Manual for Team Building*. University Associates Inc., San Diego.

Griffith, R. (2007) The importance of earnest record keeping. *Nurse Prescribing*, **5**(8), 363–6.

Plant, R. (1987) *Managing Change and Making it Stick*. Fontana Collins, London.

Stephenson, N. (2008) Self-directed learning: communication. *British Journal of Healthcare Assistants*, **2**(6), 301–3.

Learning from the NHS

I recently watched a most interesting BBC2 series of 'fly on the wall' documentaries entitled 'Can Gerry Robinson Fix the NHS?', featuring Sir Gerry Robinson, the successful management guru, as he worked for six months with Brian James, the Chief Executive of Rotherham General Hospital in Yorkshire.

The purpose of the series was to explore how the NHS can improve its overall efficiency, reduce waiting lists and address the real problems that prevent staff from implementing much needed change.

These thought-provoking documentaries identified some serious issues about how problems within the NHS hospital seem to take many months to resolve simply because everything had to go through a long and bureaucratic staff/management consultation process.

Nurses seemed prepared to cope with staff shortages because they believed there was a recruitment freeze in place throughout the hospital. However, when Brian James was confronted with the situation by frustrated nursing staff and departmental managers at a 'face-to-face' meeting, he agreed to provide the additional staff immediately. This resolved the situation and put an end to the obvious difficulties that staff had just accepted and which may have been due in part to an apparent lack of confidence in the hospital manager's ability to resolve their staffing issue at a departmental level.

All staff, whether in the NHS or the independent care sector, require strong leadership and fair management, but more importantly they need to be set realistic goals and objectives.

In my experience, all care home staff, including nurses, support workers, administrators, therapists, and catering, domestic, laundry and maintenance personnel all seem to respond positively if their managers take the time to make them feel valued and listened to. We must provide clarity in our lines of communication, providing staff with appropriate training and real support.

Empowering your staff to come up with new ideas to make things better for the residents can often result in transforming a failing care home into great care home.

We need to join together in delivering high standards of care for our residents, their families and our staff.

Management is all about getting the best out of people and creating a positive approach to the issues of the day rather than dwelling on the negative aspects. According to Sir Gerry Robinson 'The NHS needs to learn that you don't solve problems by throwing money at it, and not every problem actually needs money to solve it'. Managers need to literally 'walk the floor' of the institutions that they run, gaining an insight into life as an employee and as a patient. Only then will they be able to engage staff in the process of reforming services.

Reference

Ashurst, A. (2007) Learning from the NHS. *Nursing & Residential Care*, **9**(3), p. 93.

Key points

- Many older people living in care experience diminished sight and hearing, which naturally makes communicating more difficult. Help is available from RNID and RNIB in terms of facilitating caring environments for those with sensory loss.
- Nurses today are expected to spend a great deal of their time writing daily records on the activities and care delivered to their residents.
- How staff answer the telephone provides members of the public and potential customers with their first impression of the care home.
- Good communications are one of the essential ingredients to developing an effective and efficient care home staff team.
- Newly registered nurses often lack the experience to give instructions to more experienced care staff.
- Regular face-to-face meetings with residents and their relatives can often defuse potential problems, and the staff nurse who gets to know her residents as their named nurse can produce benefits.

Discussion points

- What management methods are currently in use through out the NHS?
- What aspects of independent care home and hospitals management could be utilised in the NHS?
- Do you and your team think that Sir Gerry Robinson is right when he says: 'The NHS needs to learn that you don't solve problems by throwing money at it, and not every problem actually needs money to solve it'?
- Managers need to literally 'walk the floor' of the institutions that they run gaining an insight into life as an employee and as a patient. Only then will they be able to engage staff in the process of reforming services.
- What are the future benefits of working in partnership with the NHS?

Public speaking and care home training sessions

Public speaking and delivering care home training sessions are skills which are increasingly being required of senior care home staff, but ones with which they may not feel immediately at ease.

In today's care home climate, day care home managers are required to provide their staff with relevant up-to-date training. As a direct result, the home manager may call upon experienced staff within the home to help put a training package together. In addition to in-house training, there is a commitment to sending staff on external courses which are organised by local training agencies.

It is important that anyone asked to speak publicly has the relevant knowledge and positive approach to deliver a clear and simple message which is both factual and thought-provoking.

The person must be confident and well motivated to carry out this task. Unfortunately, reluctant conscripts often transfer their lack of enthusiasm to the audience.

Imagine that your home manager has asked you to participate in the home's staff training day. You can choose to speak on any aspect relating to the introduction of a customer care policy within the home.

Sharing knowledge is vital if we are to learn from our mistakes. Practical case studies are useful as they allow staff to analyse mistakes and to identify better methods. Prior to the training session, you need to establish the extent of staff knowledge about customer care. Perhaps you could ask them to write down 10 key elements of positive customer care within the home. Once you have this information to hand, write the answers on a flip-chart. This can form the basis of your research and will enable you to establish the best way to progress.

It may be useful at this point to incorporate observations from the resident's relatives. These often highlight the gap between the quality of service which you think you are delivering and the quality of service delivery as perceived by the residents and their families.

Preparation

The effectiveness of any presentation can be measured by the amount of information which staff are able to recall at the end. Imparting information successfully to staff will depend largely on your preparation. It is vital that you know what you are talking about, and this may require extensive research. In carrying out any research within the home, one needs to consider the qualities needed and this policy needs to be updated and informed through training of and consultation with staff.

Ice breakers

Any form of 'ice breaker' is useful to put students undertaking any training programme in the right frame of mind for the forthcoming session. As a trainer, I often ask those people in the group to write down four important things about themselves and discuss them with the person sitting next to them. Then the person who they have been speaking to actually introduces them to the rest of the group.

There are today hundreds of 'ice breakers' available via the Internet and these are really useful to use on a regular basis.

Teaching methods

During a two-hour training session, it is advisable, after facilitating a short ice breaker, to try to use a variety of teaching methods. Initially, you may want to separate your audience into small groups and suggest that they elect a spokesperson to feedback information. The person chosen should feed back at the end of the exercise to the whole audience.

The spokesperson must ensure that the information is clear and concise and reflects the views of the whole group, rather than just the spokesperson. This encourages staff to offer their opinions and makes them feel more involved in the subject and less like they are being lectured to. Asking staff for their opinions also reduces the risk of appearing overly patronising. If staff do feel that they are being patronised, they are likely to stop paying attention.

Acetates and an overhead projector

Today acetates are often seen as old-fashioned, but some lecturers still use them in certain special cases.

Using acetates allow you to impart your information clearly, as they can be put on an overhead projector which allows everyone in the room to see. The information on the acetates should be well spaced and presented in bullet points.

Keep the information to key points only, as complex written acetates are often difficult to read and might prove counter-productive.

Appropriate DVD/video usage

Whilst researching your presentation you may find a suitable DVD/video that could be used to illustrate your key points and help to prompt a group discussion.

Watching the programme yourself is vital. Never rely on anyone else's word stating that the content is relevant, because it may not be so: this could cause you a great deal of embarrassment.

In addition, you will need to structure your talk around the programme, so you will need to know how long it is. If you decide to use a DVD/video, prepare a list of questions to ask the staff at the end of the programme. It is also helpful to link the issues raised by the DVD/video with practical examples of similar situations within your own care home. This interactive approach will have more impact on the staff than just relying on the DVD/video to identify issues for you.

Check DVD/video equipment

Always check your DVD/video equipment before the session and if you are using a television for the first time, it is very important to ensure that it works properly. You may wish to use a PowerPoint presentation which will be fed through a laptop computer and special projector.

As a precaution, try to print handouts that illustrate all your slides as a precaution against electrical equipment breaking down.

Timing

When planning your training session, ensure that you allow time for questions and debate. Questions and answers may take place throughout your session, but ideally there should be some time allocated at the end to give the staff a chance to raise any points requiring clarification.

When preparing your talk, it is a good idea to time yourself before the event so that you can determine exactly how long your presentation takes and how much time will be available for questions. You do not want to have to rush anything or leave anything out, nor do you want to be stuck with nothing to say. However, do not allow yourself to be side-tracked, as this will waste everyone's time and lead you to overrun your allocated slot, which may in turn disrupt the rest of the day's programme.

A typical training day may take many forms. A special theme is useful and the subject of customer care may be just one component of this.

The presentation

Different people prefer different methods of presentation. However, if you are not experienced in public speaking, there is a danger that you will rely too heavily on your teaching aids. It is easy to become very flustered if you lose a sheet of your notes or if your acetates fall onto the floor. Again, detailed preparation is the key here.

The better you know the subject matter within your presentation, the less flustered you will be if something goes wrong. Likewise, if you are well prepared you are sure to grow in confidence as your presentation unfolds. The video will also help to break up your talk and will provide a different medium through which staff can recognise the benefits of introducing and developing customer care. Encourage staff to discuss the contents of the video, but keep the discussions brief and to the point, because you can always revisit the issues raised at the end of the session.

Conquering your nerves

Often, even experienced public speakers suffer from nerves before important talks. Some people feel physically sick and this can only be overcome by trying to relax. You may choose to sit quietly on your own before entering the room to speak. Alternatively, you may try doing some deep breathing exercises.

The general rule is to use whatever method of relaxation works for you.

You must also remain focused on the positive aspects of your talk:

- You have planned the talk; keep it interesting and relevant to your audience.
- You have practised it and got the timing just right.
- You are among colleagues who are keen to learn.

The author speaks at an NRC conference in Birmingham.

In addition, a glass of still water by your side can be helpful to stop your mouth feeling dry and for preventing any light-headedness caused by nerves.

Time flies when you are giving a good talk and your enthusiasm for the subject will put you and your audience in the right frame of mind to retain the information you are sharing with them.

Tips for public speaking

- Speak clearly and slowly
- Avoid repetition of the subject matter
- Do not just read your notes. Try to make eye contact with the group
- Do not talk with your back to the group
- Remember: you know the beginning, middle and the end of your talk
- If you do not know an answer to a question, avoid making one up. Admit that you do not know the answer and say that you will find out the necessary information

Summary

The art of public speaking can only be mastered by years of practice, and it may be useful to watch how other speakers operate when attending courses and conferences yourself. Observing how people use acetates and how they pace their talk can give you valuable pointers to improving your own presentation skills.

Your first efforts may be daunting, but I urge you to persevere. It is worth it and I am certain that the staff and your care home manager will be grateful that you made the effort.

Remember that by sharing your knowledge you will ensure that staff follow in your footsteps and deliver high standards of customer care. Ultimately, the residents and their relatives will be the true beneficiaries of the culture of positive customer care in your home.

References

Ashurst, A. (2000) Public speaking and care home training sessions. *Nursing & Residential Care*, **2**(4), 161.

Key points

- Check DVD/video equipment and overhead projector or computer and special projector if using PowerPoint before staff enter the room.
- Organise the seating and use a variety of methods of presentation for maximum impact.
- Plan your talk and practice your delivery of the presentation.
- Keep any acetates and handouts simple.
- Encourage staff to ask questions and to give constructive feedback.

Designing your PowerPoint presentations

It is essential that you keep your PowerPoint presentations simple, clear and concise.

It is useful to remember that the PowerPoint presentation is just an extension of the old-fashioned slide show. The main advantage is that you can control what the audience actually see, and therefore you can introduce text line by line. People with experience can now even stream video clips into their presentations.

However, it is important to say that some people are claiming to suffer from a new syndrome known as 'death by PowerPoint', caused by speakers using so many slides with their presentation. At conferences and large semi-nars, where you may have to sit and listen to lots of different presentations, you can begin to get tired of watching slide after slide. In an ideal world people who deliver speeches at conferences should use a variety of methods to deliver their presentations.

Tips for successful PowerPoint presentations include:

- There should be a maximum of three short sentences on each slide.
- Use a minimum font size of 24 points so that people can read the text easily in a large room.
- Use the same typeface and colour on each slide.
- If you use clip art, use appropriate images to reinforce the message in the text.
- If you use photographs ensure that they are sharp and well exposed. Poor images can ruin a presentation.
- It would be good to have the company's logo on each slide and to use the same basic design on each slide.
- Always ensure that you put your contact details on the last slide.
- When printing out slides you can use the handouts option, which can print three slides per page with a space on the left-hand side for handwritten notes.

Learning more about PowerPoint

There are a lot of useful books currently on the market that explain how to develop your PowerPoint presentations and if you need more information you can always go online for a great choice of designs for your slides.

PowerPoint: further reading

- Habraken, J. (2006) *Brilliant PowerPoint Pocketbook*. Prentice Hall, New Jersey.
- Lowe, D. (2003) *PowerPoint 2003 for Dummies*. John Wiley & Sons, Chichester.
- Online Training Solutions Inc. (2003) *PowerPoint 2003 Step by Step*. Book/CD Package. Microsoft Press.

Key points

- It is essential that you keep your PowerPoint presentations simple, clear and concise.
- It is useful to remember that the PowerPoint is just an extension of the old-fashioned slide show.
- There are a lot of useful books currently on the market that explain how to develop your PowerPoint presentations, and if you need more information you can always go online for a great choice of designs for your slides.

CHAPTER 4

Recruiting and managing staff

Staff recruitment and selection – a simple guide

Getting the recruitment process right

The time and resources used in getting the recruitment process right will be repaid many times over. The benefits will include:

- Having the right skills – being able to deliver the service that residents and their families expect.
- Improved team working – achieving the right fit is important for developing an effective team culture.
- Growth and development – having the right people in place will allow the care home to grow and develop to meet future challenges that the care industry face in the future.

Costs of getting the recruitment process wrong

- Time and money spent on advertising, short listing, interviewing, inducting, training, managing, saying goodbye and re-hiring.
- Negative individual and team morale – this relates to the physical and emotional cost to people of having to compensate for the new person's lack of skills, attitude or inappropriate behaviour.
- Reduced performance – the effort required in managing inappropriate recruitment decisions can have a detrimental effect on overall performance.

Why do we seldom get this process right?

Care home managers are extremely busy and the time they feel they can spare for recruitment is offset by the pressure to deliver on goals and targets. Other pitfalls may include:

- Recruiting in your own likeness – just because someone thinks like you, or seems to have a similar approach to life, does not mean they are right for the specific role they are applying for.
- Getting the best of a bad bunch – a common mistake, desperation to fill the post may blind a manager to future problems.
- Basing a decision on subjectivity – how long does it take for you to make a decision on whether you like or dislike a person, and how will this influence the questions you will ask and the degree to which you will explore the person's ability to do the job?
- Time – interviewing too many people and not allowing sufficient time can affect decisions made. So can a lack of recorded information on candidates. People are a business's greatest asset. It is worth remembering that the time and energy spent on the recruitment and selection process could make the difference between the success and failure of your care business.

Recruitment consultants

At times it may be necessary to make use of recruitment consultants to find suitable candidates for management and executive posts. However, these consultants may only be used by larger care providers. The role of recruitment consultants is often complex, but remember they do have access to large databases of potential candidates for care providers to choose the best candidate for the post which their company may be finding difficulty in filling. They also sift through applicants and they may even carry out the initial interview with potential candidates. The recruitment consultant is also responsible for suggesting a short list of suitable people for the vacant post.

The box provides an example of a company – Social Care Professionals – that specialises in recruitment consultancy.

There are a number of other recruitment consultancies situated throughout the country and these can be found using the Internet.

Social Care Professionals

Candidate services
All candidates are guaranteed to receive a professional and friendly service from our team of consultants across the UK and gain immediate access to the following benefits:

- Allocated and dedicated consultants
- National coverage with a branch network
- Opportunities with exclusive contract clients
- Access to Preferred Supplier Agreements with local authorities across the United Kingdom
- Vacancy updates
- Access to project work and consultancy contracts
- Excellent rates of pay
- Holiday and sick pay
- Accident and sickness cover
- Loyalty and recommendation bonuses of up to £500
- Flexible hours
- Variety of placement
- Regular branch support
- Subsidised in-house training opportunities
- Training allowance

Client services

Permanent recruitment
Long-term solutions ensure that your organisation can grow and achieve organisational aims and objectives. We are able to provide permanent recruitment solutions through a number of options that include targeted advertising campaigns, database search and executive selection.

Executive and senior appointments
As established and experienced consultants within the sector we can provide clients with specialist services. Through your dedicated consultant you can access recruitment support for troubleshooting, service reviews, consultancy placements and building teams for new services. You will have the opportunity to meet your consultant face-to-face to discuss your specific requirements which will be managed in a strictly confidential manner.

Interim placements

At Social Care Professionals Ltd we are able to provide interim placements from one month upwards across the health and social care sector. We can provide Qualified Social Workers, Qualified Nurses, Family Centre Managers, Team Leaders, Youth workers, Housing Managers, Trained Supervised Contact Workers, and Homes Managers to work across all client groups.

Care Quality Commission

As a CQC registered provider we undertake a safe selection recruitment procedure and undertake a comprehensive induction. We offer on call services 365 days of the year, 24/7, providing support, care and nursing staff cover. We provide cover to all services and are specialist providers of staff into children's residential services, ABI, housing and mental health services.

Training

- Exceeds minimum legislation and training standards as set by the CQC, Skills for Care and HSE
- Offers flexible learning programmes to meet specialist organisational needs and supports CPD
- Provides certificates with comprehensive listing of acquired knowledge and understanding
- Evidences assessment that is cross-referenced to CIS & LDQ standards

Further information: http://www.socialcareprofessionals.co.uk; accessed 31 December 2009.

The recruitment and selection process

Identify the purpose of the job

Identifying why you are recruiting and what gaps need to be filled can be either a simple process or an extremely complex one. If recruiting for a senior role within the care home then you will need to consider the make-up of your existing care team.

It is important that you do not rush this process; the impact of the wrong appointment being made can have far-reaching consequences.

Whether to recruit or not?

Do you need to recruit at all or could you fill the position through succession planning? It may be useful to re-evaluate existing team members' roles prior to any recruitment process.

Regional Operations managers may decide to interview existing heads of care for a vacant care home manager's position, but on the other hand they may choose to bring into the company an experienced manager if the care home has particularly difficult challenges that need to be addressed as a matter of urgency.

Job and person specification

Once you have decided there is a need to recruit, you will need to review the role, create a job description and define the essential and desirable qualities through the person specification.

The person specification should help you identify:

- their capabilities
- the knowledge they need to possess
- essential attitudes or characteristics
- how they would fit into the organisation

Agree in advance with colleagues who are involved in the recruitment and selection process what is essential and what could be developed.

Recruitment

Ensure that any information on vacancies is fair, clear and accurate before it goes to potential applicants. Where possible, seek and make use of specialist expertise in relation to recruiting, selecting and ultimately retaining your colleagues.

Selection

Completed applications should be sifted to ensure that you will be interviewing only suitable candidates.

The process of selecting the right person can be accomplished through in-depth interviews and personality- and competency-based assessments.

The interview process

It is essential that the interview process is fair and consistent for all candidates. The panel members should have their questions agreed between each other before the commencing the interview.

The interview should be held in a suitable environment, as this gives the candidate a first impression of how the company treats and values potential employees.

Interview feedback

If a candidate is unsuccessful they should always be provided with constructive feedback. This may help them in their attempts to find a new post in the future.

Best practice

A best practice guide in recruitment and selection is available from:

> The Management Standards Centre
> Tel: 020 7240 2826
> Email: management.standards@managers.org.uk
> Web site: http://www.management-standards.org/

How to develop a staff appraisal system

Implementing an appraisal system

An appraisal system should be put in place within the care home in conjunction with regular staff supervision.

Home managers are responsible for ensuring that all members of the staff team receive formal feedback on their individual performance at least twice a year.

Role and function

Staff who sense that the home owner and the home manager value their contribution will be encouraged to continue performing to the best of their ability.

Staff appraisal allows the home manager to demonstrate clearly how well or how poorly the member of staff is performing.

Any deterioration identified in an individual's work performance should be dealt with immediately, as there may be certain relevant circumstances that the home manager can help resolve.

The staff appraisal system should be designed to allow staff the opportunity to agree personal objectives with the care home manager and subsequently to work towards achieving these goals. It is important that staff objectives are in line with those of the care home, i.e. not only to improve the individual's performance but also that of the care home.

Care homes using a standardised method of appraisal provide every member of staff with a checklist, which will prove useful at monthly staff development meetings.

Managers can regularly monitor team member's personal objectives. It is advisable that staff use objective action plans, to assist them in progressing in their career.

The appraisal system is not meant to be a paper exercise, and the document produced should be used on a regular basis to focus the staff on their agreed objectives. Appraisal forms gathering dust on a shelf are not worth the paper they are written on.

The time set aside in preparation by both the care home manager and the member of staff can prove essential to the success of any appraisal meeting. A blank copy of the appraisal documentation should be given to the staff member two weeks before the meeting.

Personal objectives

The personal objectives should be SMART: specific, measurable, realistic, achievable and timely. Therefore staff must be given support to complete their objectives before the appraisal meeting.

The care home manager or their deputy/Head of Care may be able to offer assistance, but should not influence the member of staff into setting themselves unrealistic objectives.

Employees undergoing appraisals are an important part of staff development and should be used to focus staff on objectives as well as to encourage further achievements.

Benefits of an appraisal system

The care home manager provides an opportunity to discuss face-to-face with each member of the staff team their personal objectives and to encourage them to develop themselves over the coming six months and beyond. There is also an opportunity to review the previous six months' performance.

It is important for both the care home manager and the member of staff that an overall review of performance takes place without prejudice.

It is useful to reflect upon both clinical and managerial practice. Registered nurses are required to keep themselves updated and the home manager can verify that they have attended a number of study days and also book training sessions for the next six months.

The action plan with regard to staff development should identify courses and subjects that are relevant to the position that the member of staff holds within the home.

The appraisal session is of benefit to the staff member because they can have a dedicated time with their manager and receive guidance and encouragement.

The care home owner may reward good performance financially; however, this is not always the case.

Documentation

It is advisable to keep the paperwork simple and clear without any ambiguity that may confuse the staff member.

One needs to ensure that both of the people involved in the meeting sign at the end of the meeting and are given the opportunity to write a brief comment about their appraisal.

Both the home manager and the member of staff must agree the future objectives.

Staff appraisal is a good method of keeping staff informed and up to date about their progress, but must not be seen as the solution to all other forms of support and development.

Care home managers will hope to retain staff that are both trained and supported throughout the year. At the staff appraisal meeting employees need to feel confident and they need to be encouraged to identify what it is they are hoping to achieve in the subsequent six months.

The meeting

The meeting should be conducted within an informal setting. Managers should ensure that there are no disturbances. Telephone calls must be diverted and any mobile phones should be switched off. Ideally a 'do not disturb' notice should be posted on the office door. It is most frustrating for both parties if there are constant interruptions during the meeting.

Staff appraisal meetings should be organised carefully to allow people the chance to exchange views and thoughts in a relaxed atmosphere with honesty and trust between both parties.

Designing the system

When care home managers design an appraisal system, they must consider the following important elements in which to measure staff performance:

- Has the member of staff been efficient and effective in their role?
- Does the individual add value to the care team?
- Has the member of staff presented objectives that are specific, measurable, achievable, realistic and timely?
- What support and training are required and can be provided by the care home manager or deputy to assist the employee to achieve their personal goals?
- How have both parties perceived and scored the individual's performance over the last 6 months?
- Does the person's performance match the expectations set out in the job description?

- Has the individual's performance exceeded the company's expectations and what is his/her potential for promotion?
- Is there an action plan for staff to follow in order to achieve their personal goals?

Appraisal scores

Some care home managers prefer to give personal scores in each area of the appraisal, with the opportunity also being given to the staff to give their own scores. However, if there is a vast difference in the scores, then there will need to be further discussion, with a compromise being agreed by the end of the meeting.

The reviewer provides an overall aggregate score and this may be used by the care home owner as an indicator to form part of a salary review at a determined point in the year. The care home manager should score the various elements of the appraisal as the meeting is proceeding.

Scoring must always be used to give staff an honest view of their overall work performance.

Action plan

Following a supervision meeting or an annual appraisal, all staff must be encouraged to formulate an action plan for the year ahead. This plan needs to include practical aspects of the staff member's work in accordance with their job description. In addition you may choose to review certain aspects of their performance on a two-monthly basis. You need to put in place strict time frames so that staff know what actions they need to complete in order to meet and exceed the standard in any area of their role. There should also be a specific section of the action plan set aside for the individual's personal learning and development pathway: this will include any mandatory training and specialised training undertaken and any training required in the future.

Discussion points

- Describe the elements of SMART goals and provide examples of each element.
- Why is it important to keep a record of all supervision and appraisal?
- Why is it vital to keep nurses up to date with clinical practice?

The successful manager carries out regular staff supervision and appraisal meetings.

Key points

- An appraisal system should be put in place within the care home in conjunction with regular staff supervision.
- Staff who sense that the home owner and the home manager value their contribution will be encouraged to continue performing to the best of their ability.
- Staff appraisal allows the home manager to demonstrate clearly how well or how poorly the member of staff is performing.

References

Ashurst, A. (2000) How to develop a staff appraisal system. *Nursing & Residential Care*, **2**(12), 596–7.

The preceptorship process

Newly registered nurses require support and ongoing feedback to maintain confidence in their skills and improve their application of theory to practice.

Commencing work as a newly registered nurse should be one of the most exciting and rewarding periods of a person's nursing career.

However, in reality some nurses are initially overwhelmed by the enormous realisation that they are personally responsible and accountable for their own practice from the point of registration, irrespective of any support system.

It is important that managers are able to identify the importance of preceptorship of staff employed to work in a care home or independent hospital.

A simple step-by-step approach to implementing an effective preceptorship plan will be described, which may prove to be beneficial both to the newly registered nurse, the residents and the rest of the multidisciplinary care team.

What is preceptorship?

Preceptorship is a specific teaching and learning strategy performed by an experienced nurse who acts as a role model and resource. The experienced nurse will have at least 12 months' experience of working in the same field as the newly registered nurse.

The aim of preceptorship is to develop competence and confidence, and to foster professional development of the newly registered nurse which is focused on the needs of the patients, residents and the service as a whole. This process is facilitated by relevant support mechanisms and the concept of continuous learning.

Cook (1996) identified:

the support available to newly Registered nurses to be provided by a number of key professionals within the care home or independent hospital. This support may include:

- Mentors: who are experienced professionals nurturing and guiding the newly registered nurse
- Clinical supervision: an exchange between practising nurses and members of the multi disciplinary team, to enable the development of professional skills
- Preceptor: a teacher or instructor. In addition nurses should receive regular formal supervision, covering all aspects of the nurses' performance, including management performance and clinical abilities.

Why is preceptorship important?

Today, newly registered nurses have the opportunity to benefit from the implementation of the preceptorship concept.

In years gone by new staff nurses usually found themselves thrown in at the deep end working in National Health Service (NHS) wards. While on day duty, there always appeared to be additional experienced nursing staff on the wards for support. Nursing was based on 'task allocation' and relied heavily on a medical nursing model. The Roper, Logan and Tierney model was favoured by many nurses in the 1970s and 80s. The consultants and ward sister or charge nurses managed the wards, and the old-fashioned matron visited the patients every day for on-the-spot face-to-face feedback.

Many changes have occurred since then. Preceptorship is important, as present-day staff nurses are now provided with a support system that can make a real difference to developing the skills required to become a competent practitioner in their own right.

Many newly registered nurses feel that their lack of knowledge regarding the residents' conditions, individual care plans and medication regimes are too much to remember all at once.

Problems surrounding forgetfulness and loss of self-esteem may lead to the nurse feeling worthless, and this can sometimes, in severe cases, lead to illness if the issues are not addressed with colleagues, including the nurse's preceptor and the care home manager or the independent hospital manager.

The manager who develops a good rapport with the team member will prove the most effective preceptor.

Providing professional support

The preceptor, along with the care home manager or hospital manager, will be experienced enough to recognise these and other examples of stress and ideally provide staff with the appropriate types of support. The nurse should also be offered professional help if necessary and provided with coping strategies to overcome the cause of their stress. Moore (2006) recognises that:

Transition from student to staff nurse is stressful. The increased responsibility, fear of litigation and accountability are some of the great fears for newly Registered nurses.

Career development

Though it is encouraged, preceptorship is not a mandatory requirement, and the Nursing and Midwifery Council (NMC) has no power to enforce the system.

The NMC Code (2008), Standards of Conduct Performance and Ethics for Nurses and Midwives, outlines what a registered nurse must do in caring for patients and clients (see box).

Key points in the NMC Code

- You must have the knowledge and skills for safe and effective practice when working without direct supervision
- You must recognise and work within the limits of your competence
- You must keep your skills and knowledge up to date throughout your working life
- You must take part in appropriate learning and practice activities that maintain and develop your competence and performance
- You must treat people as individuals and respect their dignity
- You must act as an advocate for those in your care, helping them to access relevant health and social care, information and support
- You must respect people's right to confidentiality
- You must listen to the people in your care and respond to their concerns and preferences
- You must make arrangements to meet people's language and communication needs
- You must share with people, in a way they can understand, the information they want to know about their health

Nursing Times, 29 April 2008, **104**(17); http://www.nursingtimes.net/

Concerning preceptors, the NMC (2006) suggests:

They may work full time or part time but must be able to show willingness and aptitude for the role and must be keen to share their knowledge and skills. They should also understand and support the concept of preceptorship and be aware of the additional demands which it places upon them.

A preceptor must be:

- an experienced and competent role model, working within the care home or independent hospital
- able to demonstrate skills to undertake supportive 1:1 teaching and develop a learning relationship with the newly qualified staff nurse
- able to support newly registered nurses providing feedback to help them maintain their confidence and to improve their skills

The NMC (2006) encourages a period of preceptorship to facilitate newly qualified nurses' entry into first level registration:

All newly registered nurses should be provided with a period of support (approximately 4–6 months) under the guidance of a preceptor.

The preceptorship process is a formative one, during which the knowledge, skills and attitudes acquired during pre-registration are applied to practice.

Preceptorship will ensure that responsibilities are not excessive or given prematurely to the practitioner, therefore enhancing care and protection for the patients and/or residents. It is recognised that this period of transition can be most stressful, as new demands are placed on the new nurse.

Coping with work-related stress

Taking on such a responsible new role can be stressful for the nurse. On a practical basis it is important that the employer accepts that stress in nurses can manifest itself in many different ways, including lack of sleep and worrying constantly both at work and at home.

Some nurses may feel the need to resort to drinking alcohol in an endeavour to relax when they get home from work. This may lead in some cases, to nurses developing a drinking habit which ultimately requires medical treatment and support.

Another symptom is irritability with colleagues, friends and family, which may lead to arguments and the breakdown of personal relationships.

A close team of colleagues at work should be able to provide support to the staff.

Temper outbursts at work and at home cause distress not just for the newly registered nurses, but also to those around them. Sometimes nurses feel frustration and this may lead to other problems if not checked and dealt with by a line manager.

Loss of concentration can be a common problem among some newly registered nurses. They find themselves repeatedly having to check up on things: reassurance and support are therefore essential ingredients to help other newly registered nurses may suffer from a loss of confidence, requiring support from senior colleagues

Staff nurses have a continuing professional responsibility and are accountable for all their own actions and omissions from the day they are admitted onto the register.

It must be remembered that the preceptor cannot be accountable for the actions of newly Registered nurses.

However, one of the important benefits of preceptorship for newly registered nurses is that they can receive personal assistance in helping them to apply their theoretical knowledge to up to date clinical practice.

References

Ashurst, A. (2008) Career development: 'The preceptorship process'. *Nursing & Residential Care*, **10**(6), 307–9.

Cook, R. (1996) Clinical Supervision: a talking shop? *Practice Nursing*, **7**(15), 12–13.

Moore, C. (2006) The transition from student to registered nurse: a military perspective. British Journal of Nursing, **15**(10), 540–2.

Nursing and Midwifery Council (NMC) (2006) *Standards to Support Learning and Assessment in Practice*. NMC, London.

Nursing and Midwifery Council (NMC) (2008) *Standards of Conduct Performance and Ethics for Nurses and Midwives*. http://www.nmc-uk.org/; accessed 15 November 2009.

Key points

- Preceptorship is a specific teaching and learning strategy performed by an experienced nurse who acts as a role model and resource.
- The preceptorship process is formative: in which the knowledge, skills and attitudes acquired during pre-registration are applied to practice.
- Transition from student to staff nurse is stressful. The increased responsibility, fear of litigation and accountability are some of the great fears for newly registered nurses.
- The preceptor cannot be accountable for the actions of newly registered nurses.

Discussion points

- Discuss the reasons why preceptorship is important for newly qualified staff.
- Discuss the methods of preceptorship that are in place within your workplace.

The consequences of whistle blowing

In April 2009, the BBC recently aired a 'fly on the wall' documentary *Panorama: Britain's Home Care Scandal*. The programme highlighted some areas of serious concern affecting vulnerable people living in the community and requiring regular care and support. Two undercover care workers and the *Panorama* team were able to expose serious flaws in the delivery of domiciliary care services for older people.

Some of the issues highlighted included:

- Care staff not receiving adequate training before commencing domiciliary care work and learning 'on the job' from other carers, often seen cutting corners owing to pressure of work and time factors.
- Poor and out-of-date care plans, or in some cases, non-existent individualised care plans and medicine records, leading to confusion and poor communication.
- Care staff displaying an unprofessional approach and attitude by talking on their mobile phones while attempting to carry out sensitive care duties for the service user.

Several weeks after the programme was aired, Margaret Haywood, a registered nurse, was struck off the Nursing and Midwifery Council (NMC) register for breaching patient confidentiality.

Between November 2004 and May 2005 Ms Haywood covertly filmed elderly patients on a ward at Brighton and Sussex University Hospitals NHS Trust for the *Panorama* documentary.

Linda Nazarko, a much respected nurse, author and NRC board member, recently took part in a debate surrounding the case and made some very important points.

As nurses we go where others cannot. We perform intimate care. We see people at their sickest and most vulnerable. We often care for people at their lowest ebb. People tell us their deepest darkest secrets. They trust us. Margaret Haywood performed her duties with a camera concealed in her uniform. She filmed sick vulnerable older people some of whom were dying. In secretly filming vulnerable older people Margaret Haywood breached that trust.

Whistle blowing is not a new phenomenon and the consequences to the whistle blowers themselves can in some cases be far-reaching and life-changing.

The landmark case of the famous whistle blower charge nurse Graham Pink is worth examining (Pink and Brindle, 1990). However, I believe that today care providers must heed the warning signs if employees choose to express their concerns either verbally or in writing to senior managers. Allegations of poor practice must always be robustly investigated and action taken as and when necessary.

Failure to act in the resident's best interest may result in serious consequences for care homes. We must never become complacent, and resident's privacy, dignity and confidentiality must be maintained at all times.

References

Ashurst, A. (2009) The consequences of whistle blowing. *Nursing & Residential Care*, **11**(6), 274.

BBC (2009) *Panorama: Britain's Home Care Scandal*. 9 April. BBC, London.

Nazarko, L. (2009) Comment on: NMC defends decision to strike off undercover nurse Margaret Haywood. *Nursing Times.net*. http://tinyurl.com/d5qrmg; accessed 6 May 2009.

Pink, G. and Brindle, D. (1990) Yours sincerely, FG Pink. *The Guardian*, 15 April. http://www.guardian.co.uk/society/1990/apr/11/guardiansocietysupplement; accessed 6 May 2009.

Who cares during suspension?

We live and work in difficult times, where complaints are regularly made against care staff, not only by a resident's relatives, but also by colleagues. There is a need to handle these complaints seriously and efficiently, which inevitably leads to suspending staff from duty in order to carry out investigations impartially.

Perhaps one of the most traumatic events in any person's career is that he or she one day faces up to the realisation of suspension from duty. It is hard to imagine the impact that it must have on the person's self-esteem, confidence and physical and mental health. While there is a need for disciplinary procedures to be implemented, a system should always be put in place that protects those staff suspended from duty.

In order for any detailed and comprehensive investigation to take place, colleagues are not allowed to contact the person who has been suspended from duty. As a result, the person will feel totally isolated from his or her work colleagues, residents and other professionals with whom he or she has regular contact.

While staff maybe suspended on full pay pending any investigation, nevertheless, the impact of suspension can be both traumatic and life changing.

One must always recognise the fact that in many cases, the member of staff that suffers suspension may be innocent of all charges. It is wrong that the system of suspension can often result in people facing many weeks of doubt and uncertainty about their future working lives. The only support that a member of staff who is suspended can rely on is his or her own family and close friends.

Who, if anyone, from the employer is responsible for ensuring that the accused member of staff is given support and guidance during the period of suspension?

The suspended person should be encouraged to consult his or her GP and a person not associated in the case should be available for confidential support. Some companies do have a 24-hour confidential helpline for staff.

As weeks go by without a result of the investigation being known, the suspended person's health can quickly deteriorate. Healthcare companies should adopt a simple support system that guarantees this person the opportunity of discussing his or her case with a senior manager within four weeks of being suspended. This would give the person the opportunity to discuss his or her feelings and emotions with a qualified professional.

Who, if anyone, cares for staff suspended from duty in your organisation? Is there a better and fairer way of handling those staff that face suspension?

We all have 'a duty of care' to support the staff who provide an excellent service to others. One day, every reader may face the awful prospect of suspension from duty.

Reference

Ashurst, A. (2004) Who cares during suspension. *Nursing & Residential Care*, **6**(8), 365.

Discussion points

- The suspension of staff must be handled sensitively and the HR department kept fully informed.
- How can the manager ensure that staff are supported through suspension?
- Why is it important for staff to be suspended if allegations have been raised?

The NMC Code of Conduct

Standards of conduct, performance and ethics for nurses and midwives
This Code was approved by the NMC's Council on 6 December 2007 and implemented on 1 May 2008.

The people in your care must be able to trust you with their health and wellbeing.

To justify that trust, you must

- make the care of people your first concern, treating them as individuals and respecting their dignity
- work with others to protect and promote the health and wellbeing of those in your care, their families and carers, and the wider community
- provide a high standard of practice and care at all times
- be open and honest, act with integrity and uphold the reputation of your profession

As a professional, you are personally accountable for actions and omissions in your practice and must always be able to justify your decisions.

You must always act lawfully, whether those laws relate to your professional practice or personal life.

Failure to comply with this Code may bring your fitness to practise into question and endanger your registration.

This Code should be considered together with the Nursing and Midwifery Council's rules, standards, guidance and advice available from:

Nursing & Midwifery Council
23 Portland Place
London WIB IPZ
Tel: 020 7333 9333 email: advice@nmc-uk.org

Managing difficult people

Perhaps one of the most challenging aspects of management is dealing with difficult people.

There are many incidents that occur in a care home that can result in confrontation and the secret is for the manager to pre-empt issues occurring on a daily basis.

Residents and relatives

Everyone who has ever worked in a care setting can remember a difficult resident and or a difficult relative. So let us examine why this group of people usually complain.

The most common cause of complaint is the laundry, closely followed by the food, and if not dealt with professionally and promptly these issues can very quickly escalate.

Relatives may be reluctant to make a complaint on behalf of the resident, as they are concerned of the consequences of complaining to the manager.

Relatives may complain about the lack of information they receive from the care home staff, so it is important to arrange regular clinical reviews. Some care home managers hold weekly surgeries where they can see relatives at a specific time, usually in the evening. This regular feedback provides relatives with an opportunity to air their grievances before they become major complaints.

Suppliers

Suppliers complain when they do not get paid on time. Therefore good managers will always arrange for their local suppliers to be paid on time every month. The loss of a local supplier may damage the care home's reputation locally if the supplier (e.g. the butcher) chooses to tell his other customers about your reluctance to pay your invoices on time. A good reputation may take years to build, but only moments to lose.

The case of Gerald Ratner speaking to the Institute of Directors many years ago resulted in his company shares crashing. The impact of one off-hand remark had a profound impact on his jewellery business.

Staff

In my experience, staff may complain about a number of issues, but the most common is their salary.

Efficient administrators can often pre-empt complaints about staff salaries by checking time sheets diligently and advising staff about their pay.

Staff can sometimes complain about their rotas, holidays and many other issues, and the effective manager can deal with these areas of concern by holding regular staff meetings.

Good two-way communication is vital in order to pick up any unhappiness within the care home staff team, and the manager should listen carefully to what is being said and take the appropriate action to make the team work in harmony.

Disciplinary procedures

Every company have a set of disciplinary policies and procedures to follow. Managers should always be careful to follow the rules of the company they work for. Remember that deviating from the rules laid down may adversely affect the outcome of the disciplinary action.

In broad terms it is important to treat staff with respect and allow them the opportunity to hear the evidence and allegations made against them.

Performance management

Sometimes a member of staff may fail to make the grade. If this happens the manager must discuss their performance in private and make a note in their personnel file.

It is important to agree an action plan to help the member of staff regain their confidence and recognise that the manager will support them in improving their performance.

It must be remembered that staff who are being performance managed must be given a realistic time frame to get things right.

During the time when staff are under additional scrutiny it is important that the manager and staff member meet on a regular basis to discuss progress. It is disappointing when staff fail to reach an acceptable standard of performance; however, in the serious business of caring for vulnerable people, it is important that staff recognise the importance of delivering a high standard of care and hotel services. The care home manager has a 'duty of care' and responsibility to protect residents when certain staff display a poor attitude and approach to their role and the people they care for.

Resolving conflict in the workplace

Managers face many issues and incidents through out their career. When conflicts occur, it is important that the manager has a strategy to deal with the incident in a fair and even-handed manner.

Conflicts are like accidents: they are always a sequence of events. A conflict may just start by a member of staff feeling that they have been treated unfairly.

The manager needs to be seen by the staff to be impartial. Having favourite colleagues can often lead to problems and managers who socialise regularly with their colleagues leave themselves wide open to criticism.

CHAPTER 5

Marketing a care home or care facility

Marketing your care home/increasing occupancy

All care home managers have a responsibility to their employers to maximise the potential of the home. They need to have a clear understanding of marketing and how it can be utilised to best effect. The elements of marketing, known as the 'marketing mix', can be defined as:

The right product at the right price in the right place, promoted to the right people within agreed financial constraints, e.g. at a profit.

The right product

The kind of service offered by the home depends on the terms of the registration, e.g. the type of client for which the home is registered.

Market research will help identify what services are required in the local area. The care home manager must identify local competitors and discover the reasons for their success while aiming to improve his or her care home's share of the market.

The right price

There is an ongoing debate throughout the care industry concerning pricing of all care services, in both the public and independent sectors.

The true cost of 'nursing care' will only be resolved when criteria for such care are established and agreed by all parties. Hotel services in the home must also be costed accurately to achieve a realistic fee level.

In the future, detailed breakdowns of costs will be demanded by purchasers of care looking to provide best value for money.

The right place

When clients and their families are choosing a home they can be influenced greatly by its location, the community surrounding the home, the ease of access to local amenities and the transport routes available to relatives visiting the home who are reliant on public transport.

The appearance of the 'front of house' is important, as this is the first impression that people get of the home The gardens, building and car parking facilities are key features which may attract clients.

Promotion to the right people

Promotion of the home may be achieved in a number of ways, e.g. through regular news items published in local newspapers about interesting events within the home. Staff dealing professionally with telephone enquiries can also help promote the home in a positive manner. Inviting potential clients to visit can stimulate their interest in the home. Brochures sent to prospective clients must outline briefly the types of services that the home has to offer. Any claims made in brochures need to be substantiated by evidence.

Key influencers

Commissioning managers, social workers, general practitioners and ward sisters/charge nurses are often influential regarding a client's choice of care home after hospital. Organising study days in the home attracts such people to visit and can actually stimulate their interest in the services you provide.

Loss of occupancy

Managers who say they do not need to market their home often fail to build relationships with potential purchasers of care, who then may choose alterna-

Dr Tony Romero, Cambian Group's Clinical Director; one of the key speakers at a Cambian conference.

Delegates attending one of Cambian's national conferences.

tive homes. The result may be a drop in occupancy and loss of a good reputation.

Agreed financial constraints

The care home manager has overall control of the day-today costs of running the care home and must be aware of the revenue generated by the care home on a weekly basis.

Summary

In order to successfully market a quality care service there needs to be some form of audit carried out to ensure that the home is being run efficiently.

Purchasers of care will often ask to see the most recent inspection report which identifies the home's successes and shortcomings.

Marketing is only the first step in the successful delivery of any care service. Promises should never be made to provide any service which cannot be achieved. In a marketing culture, all staff will be personally involved in promoting the service in a warm and friendly manner.

Effective marketing can lead to an increase in occupancy and an enhanced local reputation throughout the community.

Handling enquiries/referrals

One of the most important aspects of increasing the care home's occupancy is to ensure that all enquiries from potential residents are handled effectively. As the care home manager you are responsible for creating the right atmosphere for people who want to visit with a view to moving their older relatives into your care home.

It is important that your vacant rooms are regularly decorated and always available for viewing. Rooms that are poorly decorated are a lot more difficult to sell to prospective residents and their families.

As the care home manager you may not always be the best person to show visitors to the care home around, but you should always ensure that you meet potential residents and their families.

The Internet has meant that many of your competitors may have their own websites with online booking forms for people to complete in the comfort of their own homes.

Developing your own website

There are many professional web designers, and in order to save many hours of your own labour it is advisable to purchase the services of a professional web designer. If you need to work to a tight budget then you can help by writing all your own copy for the website.

Imagine you are looking for a care home for a family member. You have a limited budget so your options must remain realistic. It is essential to use photographic images that portray a positive view of your home. If you use staff and residents you need to get all people featured to sign a model release form to state that they do not mind their image being used to promote your care home.

Before you start creating your website it is important to check out your competitor's websites for any ideas.

A story board of photographs may include the following photographs as standard:

- Exterior photograph showing any gardens and views of surrounding area
- Reception area and lounges
- Hairdressing salon/dining room
- *En suite* bedrooms and any special features of your care home
- Feature some of your staff with residents – undertaking social and leisure activities

In addition you should include your care home's mission statement and some short testimonials from residents and their families.

Keep your website colourful and interesting, as you must always remember that your competitors will also be creating their own websites.

You can include an online booking form which must be acted upon as soon as possible – within at a maximum of one working day. If your staff fail to respond to website enquiries, then in many cases the enquirer will just move on to the next website. We live in a 24 hour service society and people today cannot seem to wait for anything.

Developing a care home brochure

For many years the brochure has been the main marketing tool for hundreds of care homes. Some companies spend thousands of pounds to develop beautiful brochures. Following a telephone enquiry you should always send out a brochure to extol the virtues of your care home.

Ideally you should use the same photographs and copy in your care home's brochure as on your website.

Remember in both media to place a small location map and directions of how to find your care home. Not everyone actually owns a car, so details of local public transport are very important to relatives and friends. How close are you to motorways, railway stations and local amenities?

The brochure should be professionally printed. Ensure that all copy is spell checked and grammatically correct before publication.

References

Ashurst, A. (2001) Marketing your care home. *Nursing & Residential Care*, **3**(8), 398.

Making a corporate DVD

Today, many successful care providers have chosen to invest in a specialist film-making company to producing a DVD that can help to promote their profile to a large audience.

Having viewed a number of corporate DVDs it is clear to see the benefit of hiring a specialist company to develop a script and story board, and to produce the film using professional camera and sound operators, in addition to carrying out the post-production work.

Some care providers may also choose to employ professional presenters to narrate and raise various questions with the staff. Presenters may work in television or radio and they often possess the necessary experience and excellent communication skills required to make a very successful short film.

By choosing some of your existing staff to feature in the production of the DVD it is possible to portray the passion of the whole multidisciplinary team. It is vital to choose people who communicate clearly and present well on camera.

A good example of this technique can be seen in the successful B&Q TV advertising campaign where employees of the B&Q DIY chain are often used to tell the story of the store's purpose. Using actors to portray the same story may not be as effective.

The script and storyboard

It is important that you agree the script and storyboard before commencing any filming. Hiring professional camera crews can be very expensive; therefore this is another good reason to choose a professional presenter.

The script should be factual and show the key parts of your care business in the best light. The script should be signed off and agreed prior to the shoot being arranged.

Agree the location and what you propose to show. Remember that this is a partnership. If you have ever seen the reality TV show *The Apprentice* you will appreciate how small films can be a great success or an unmitigated disaster.

On location: making The Cambian Group DVD, which can be viewed at http://www. cambianhealthcare.com/ website.

Excellent forward planning and good communications with all parties concerned with the film will help to make the shooting of the film easier.

Filming a short three minute film usually takes between one and two days to complete.

Post-production work will take additional time depending on the amount of editing that is required.

Once the promotional film is completed, the care provider may choose to place it on their website.

This means that potential purchasers of care can view the film at any time, once they have accessed the care provider's website.

DVDs should always be kept as short as possible, with a simple message that explains succinctly the care provider's mission statement and vision.

The power of the media

Today many care homes and large corporate care providers throughout the country can find themselves suffering from a great deal of negative media coverage. We live in a society where access to news is instantly available 24 hours a day; therefore, such negative coverage is instantly available and widely disseminated.

I remain very concerned that the unacceptable actions of a small number of care staff seem to attract such negative and damaging media headlines. Sometimes cases of bad practice in the NHS and the independent care sector are prematurely featured in the media, long before these serious matters and allegations are fully investigated by the employers and the appropriate regulatory bodies. This can cause distress to residents, relatives and staff.

Promoting community partnerships can be beneficial to care homes. Managers who actively promote their care homes in the local community by working in close partnership with local charities, schools and colleges should be encouraged to produce press releases with captioned photographs, and provide local newspaper editors with ready-made copy. Receiving good press coverage can help care homes balance the public's perception about their place in the community.

Older people and their families need to be reassured that all the negative media publicity concerning care homes actually relates to only a tiny number of cases. There must be no hiding place for nurses and carers who fail to maintain the high standards that our residents and their families deserve. However, trials by the media are unacceptable, and care staff must think about the worst possible consequence of any actions before they make them.

Every registered care home must have a robust complaints procedure in place, and a 'whistle blower's policy' that can be activated at any time. Bringing care homes or large corporate care providers into disrepute is thankfully rare; however, we must remain vigilant in ensuring that all our staff are adequately trained and supervised.

A negative story in the media concerning your care home can have a serious detrimental effect on your future business and reputation.

There are many activities that are worthy of reporting, these may include your care home's summer fayre, a resident's special birthday, staff carrying out a sponsored walk for a local charity, Children in Need or Red Nose Day, or sponsoring the local school's netball or football team – the list is endless.

With a little imagination you can capture the interest of the local media and begin to redress the balance of negative publicity.

If your good news stories are featured at least once a month, then people could discover the reality of the very special care that you provide every day for residents and their families. If you have recently put your care home in the media spotlight, then why not share your success?

Reference

Ashurst, A. (2007) The power of the media. *Nursing & Residential Care*, **9**(8), 345.

Key points

- It is important that your vacant rooms are regularly decorated and always available for viewing.
- There are many professional web designers, and in order to save many hours of your own labour it is advisable to purchase the services of one to create your website.
- With a little imagination you can capture the interest of the local media and begin to redress the balance of negative publicity.

Discussion points

- Has your care home ever been featured in the local newspaper?
- Do you know the name of your local reporter of the local newspaper editor's name?
- Discuss with your staff what stories the local newspaper may be interested in.
- Have any of your staff carried out some exceptional service or been successful in reaching their NVQ?

CHAPTER 6

Current management challenges

Rehabilitation for older people: the multidisciplinary team

Many older people, after suffering from a long-standing medical condition, illness or injury, are discharged from hospital into a care home setting for a short period of rehabilitation (up to six weeks), which may enable them to return to their own home and family.

Rehabilitation aims to help older people to:

■ Re-build their confidence and self-esteem, which may have been affected, for example as the direct result of a recent accident.
■ Learn new practical skills which will give them the opportunity to live independently at home.

The multidisciplinary team (MDT) is usually made up of the general practitioner – (GP), nurses, occupational therapist, physiotherapist and specially trained care support staff.

The care home manager is responsible for heading up the MDT and ensuring that the individual resident's pre-assessment needs are identified clearly and realistic objectives are set. The manager also monitors and audits the day-to-day work carried out by all team members.

The physiotherapist and occupational therapist work alongside the manager, nurses and GP to agree the way in which each person's programme of therapy, activities and exercise is put into place.

The manager arranges the MDT clinical review meetings, which are held weekly to discuss the resident's progress. At a clinical review meeting the daily resident's records, care plans and results achieved by each resident are carefully analysed and any changes required are discussed by everyone present.

Previously, this type of meeting only involved the input of nursing staff and a GP, but today the introduction of physiotherapists and occupational thera-pists means that there is now the opportunity to provide residents with a truly person-centred approach to rehabilitation with positive results.

One of the manager's key roles is training staff members in the special skills that are required to work as part of the MDT. Staff that have been trained for many years in caring and doing things for older people are suddenly con-fronted with the reality of promoting older people's independence.

Undertaking rehabilitation programmes for residents means giving the care assistants a new mindset, as they are no longer expected to do everything for individuals but must encourage and provide residents with the opportunity to carry out tasks for themselves.

The nursing staff

Nurses play an important role in the delivery of nursing care over a 24-hour period of time, and often the night staff can discover information that the staff have not learnt about an individual resident.

Night staff may feel marginalised as they do not have the benefit of work-ing with the other members of the MDT. Missing out on all the team briefings and clinical reviews may result in night staff feeling left out of the rehabilita-tion process. Therefore it is important that night staff always receive relevant up-to-date information at every handover between shifts, and they should be encouraged to contribute to the overall care plan and not be simply looked upon as support staff.

Daily records of nursing interventions must remain factual and relevant, but the days of nurses writing 'Good night, slept well' should be confined to history, as the night staff can now provide much more insight into the reha-bilitation process. Night staff should be encouraged to identify if any of the residents are anxious about returning to their own homes or if they are strug-gling to understand what people expect of them in the rehabilitation process. Well-trained night staff can provide much needed reassurance and support to residents. The night provides a less busy environment for staff to take the time to extract information from residents and gives them the opportunity to openly discuss their fears and hopes for the future.

Nurses play an important role in the ordering, administration and storage of medicines. They are also involved in the positive drive to encourage residents who are considered able to administer their own medicines. Residents who can self-medicate are more likely to comply with their medicines regime when they return to their own homes, rather than having to rely on family and friends to administer medicines on a daily basis. Nurses are responsible for assessing the needs of each resident and formulating a care plan with a time-scale by which residents should be supported and encouraged to achieve the goals set for them. As key players in the rehabilitation process, nurses have a 24-hour overview of the resident and therefore a wealth of knowledge and information, which they can then go on to communicate to the rest of the MDT members. It is this type of communication that lies at the heart of any successful MDT.

Nurses also play an important part in keeping relatives informed of any progress that the resident has made and building up that success by providing the relatives with reassurance of what to expect when their relative is discharged. Providing relatives with up-to-date and relevant information of where they can find assistance if required reduces the level of stress surrounding the discharge of any resident from the care home back into the community. Relatives should also be encouraged to use and access the Internet and useful websites as a source of information. Brochures and leaflets on state welfare benefits can also be kept at the care home.

Well-informed relatives are usually satisfied relatives, and this means that they are less likely to complain if they are kept up-to-date with the progress of their loved one. Nurses are also responsible for ensuring that the residents are in the right place at the right time. Occupational therapists and physiotherapists have a limited amount of time in the home each week and therefore their schedules are carefully programmed. If residents are late in attending a therapy session then the rest of the residents' programme may be delayed. Each resident will have a daily planner and the nurse will ensure that all staff are aware of what is planned for the individual resident on each day. Nurses must also evaluate their care and note any therapy interventions that take place. This ability to report professional findings is pivotal to the success of any MDT effort.

The General Practitioner

Older people living in care homes may be associated with a higher GP workload than others of a similar age and sex (Groom *et al.*, 2000). This study, carried out in Nottinghamshire, indicated that care home residents had more face-to-face contacts in normal surgery hours. GPs can play an important role in ensuring that residents are given the correct medication and medical treatment, when they are admitted into care homes and may also be able to review the medication regime before residents are discharged home.

One of the main advantages of having the GP at a review meeting is that they can discuss, with other professionals, the effects that certain medication may be having on the residents. All important medical decisions concerning residents are not taken in isolation, but backed up with written evidence. A GP who plays an active role in the MDT may be willing to provide staff with training, giving members an insight into how to improve their observational skills, which in turn will help them to identify older people's medical conditions and ensure that there is appropriate medical intervention. Ultimately, this may prevent unnecessary calls to the GP surgery.

The physiotherapist

The care home owner may decide to employ a physiotherapist on a part-time basis, perhaps three days a week. The physiotherapist is able to assist and train older people to regain their mobility, especially after a hip replacement or after suffering from a stroke.

The physiotherapist trains care home staff to carry out passive movements and also provides advice on the correct way to move and handle residents safely, using the variety of hoisting equipment available.

The physiotherapist keeps records of their interventions with the residents and these reports form part of the evidence-based practice, which is made available to the purchasers of care.

Report writing forms an important part of the physiotherapist's workload and this time needs to be factored into their busy schedule.

The occupational therapist

Once again, the care home may employ an occupational therapist on a part-time basis, usually four days per week, and it is important that some of the time is devoted to the clinical review meetings.

In the introduction to standards 12–15 of the *Care Homes for Older People: National Minimum Standards*, the Department of Health (2002) states that:

> Many residents will need special support and assistance in engaging activities of daily life.

The occupational therapist teaches care assistants about the importance of working with residents and encouraging them to do things for themselves, including everyday tasks such as making drinks and snacks. In this way, care staff can complement the occupational therapy component of the rehabilitation programme by reinforcing the routine for each individual resident.

Just as for physiotherapists, report writing forms an important part of the workload, and time devoted to this must be agreed in advance with the manager of the care home.

The occupational therapist is responsible for liaising with the community team before discharging any resident. It may be necessary to have some adaptations made to the person's home and therefore the assessments must be made as soon as possible after admission to the home. This may also involve the assessment of the individual's ability to carry out simple day-to-day tasks such as accessing public transport or going shopping.

The activities coordinator

The care home's vibrant atmosphere is usually generated as a direct result of the activities that are taking place on a daily basis. Arranging shopping trips and outings to local places of interest all takes time to organise, but the reputation of the home will be enhanced by evidence of the activities that take place.

The activities coordinator needs resources for use with the residents, and should not be seen as a poor relation to the occupational therapist but as a separate asset to the MDT. The activities coordinator needs to be given a separate budget to ensure that they can organise trips out into the community for residents. Various group activities may also be carried out and it is important that the activities coordinator communicates with all relatives about generating new ideas for visits and arranging functions within the home.

The catering team

The chef and the catering team play a vital role in the rehabilitation process as they can provide residents with a well-balanced diet and give advice on menu planning and the special art of preparing meals for residents when they return home.

Rehabilitation can be tiring for the individual resident, so meals should form a welcome break from therapy programmes during the day. Plenty of fresh fruit and a variety of soft drinks should be made available upon request to residents.

The administrator

The administrator works behind the scenes to ensure that the care home manager is fully supported in organising the day-to-day management of the home, and also plays an important role in organising clinical reviews and ensuring the MDT are well briefed about any changes in the schedule.

A good working relationship is essential between the home manager and administrator as they both share a great deal of sensitive information.

Conclusion

The development of MDTs in care homes can provide some residents with the opportunity to return to their own homes. However, there are many residents living in care homes for which discharge back into the community is no longer a realistic option. The opportunity to provide some residents with a short-term rehabilitation programme in the care home should never place the rest of the residents at a disadvantage.

Employing physiotherapists and occupational therapists enables the care home to provide specialist services and this should be reflected in the weekly fees. This balance can be achieved successfully as every care home is measured by the results it achieves for both the residents and their families.

Working within an MDT is rewarding and provides staff with great job satisfaction and should one day become the benchmark for all care homes to aspire to.

References

Ashurst, A. (2006) Rehabilitation for older people: the multi-disciplinary team. *Nursing & Residential Care*, **8**(10), 456–8.

Department of Health (2002) *Care Homes for Older People: National Minimum Standards*, 2nd edn. HMSO, London.

Groom, L., Avery, A. J., Boot, D., O'Neill, C., Thornhill, K., Brown, K. and Jones, R. (2000) The impact of nursing home patients on general practitioners' workload. *British Journal of General Practice*, **50**, 473–6.

Key points

- Well-informed relatives are usually satisfied relatives, and this means that they are less likely to complain if they are kept up to date with the progress of their loved one.
- A good working relationship is essential between the home manager and administrator, as they both share a great deal of sensitive information.
- Working within a MDT is rewarding and provides staff with great job satisfaction and should one day become the benchmark for all care homes to aspire to.

Discussion points

- How would you manage potential conflict between professional team members?
- Why should the MDT members all have an input into the residents' care planning process?
- Discuss the advantages of having a multidisciplinary team approach to care and support for carers and their families.

Learning from the Zimmers

In 2007 the BBC broadcast a most moving documentary, *Power to the People*, made by Tim Samuels (BBC 2, 28 May 2007). The fascinating documentary followed the Zimmers, a group of 40 older people, including some centenarians, who recorded The Who's classic 1960s song *My Generation*. The Zimmers have now gone on to gain worldwide fame and recognition.

The documentary did much more than follow these interesting people on a journey of discovery. The film proved to me once and for all that age alone should never be a barrier to achieving your personal goals.

Older people in our society today often suffer from loneliness, poverty, illness and social isolation.

Among some of the real life characters we met in the documentary were Joan Bennett, who in her 60s was living alone in a small flat in London. Aside from her routine visits to the GP, she had not left her home for three years. Eric Whitty, aged 69, lives in a care home near Liverpool, he loves karaoke and can often be found singing anything from the Beatles to Elvis.

We also met Winifred Warburton, aged 99, who revealed that she had moved 16 times in an endeavour to find a care home that keeps her stimulated. She currently lives in a care home in Derbyshire. Winifred worked as a journalist when she was younger, she loves poetry, and is busy writing her memoirs at present.

How many Joans, Erics and Winifreds do you know? As care home managers and staff who are engaged in working with older people living in care homes, we must always remain committed and passionate about the care and support we provide.

Why would any of our residents wish to move into another care home if we motivate them and treat them with respect and dignity, as we would expect to be treated ourselves? We can make a real difference to our residents' lives by generating an atmosphere of challenge and stimulation for those who want to participate in varied daily activity programmes. Some older people suffering from dementia may become much too frail to be involved in any activities; however, I strongly believe that everyone, regardless of age, should be given a chance to participate in appropriate and enjoyable activities.

Power to The People demonstrated to me that if people are well motivated to reach out of their comfort zone they can achieve great things. I am confident that there are hundreds of care homes nationwide with vibrant activities programmes being delivered throughout every week of the year. The successful care homes share good practice and communicate with their residents' relatives and friends.

Arranging day trips and shopping trips for our care home residents can be very demanding, time-consuming and hard work, but the positive results so often achieved far outweigh the downsides.

The lasting impression that I took away from this excellent documentary is a hope for society to recognise that growing old should not be seen as the end of the road, but the beginning of a new journey.

Reference

Ashurst, A. (2007) Learning from the Zimmers. *Nursing & Residential Care*, **9**(9), 397.

Defending independent care

I recently read an advertisement by Unison in a national newspaper that featured a photograph of a large house divided into two. One half of the house was well maintained and titled 'public care home'; the other half was boarded up, with a sign that stated 'sold for redevelopment', and titled 'private don't care home'. Underneath the advertisement were the words

> When private companies run public services, they do it more for their own profit than for the benefit of the public. Over the past five years, it's led to the loss of over 50 000 care home places. In short, Britain's elderly are being sold down the river.

> Private companies running public services, which side are you on?

Angered by the advertisement, I complained to the Advertising Standards Authority (ASA). I was not alone.

One hundred and forty private and voluntary care homes, their trade associations and members of the public had also objected to the advertisement.

The ASA decided that the advertisers had not substantiated the implication that 50,000 care home places had been lost because of the greed of private care homes. As such, the advertisement was deemed to be misleading and likely to cause serious or widespread offence. The ASA concluded that it could incite undue fear and distress among residents of private care homes.

The advertisers were instructed to discontinue the advertisement and avoid such an approach in the future.

The ASA's full adjudication of 28 August 2002 can be found on their website: http://www.asa.org.uk/.

Having worked in the independent care sector in a variety of senior management positions since 1990, I am acutely aware of the perception among certain sections of the community that private care providers are driven only by profit. There are thousands of committed staff working in the independent care sector throughout the country. Staff deliver high-quality care, not only to elderly people but also to younger people with mental illness and learning disabilities. In addition to care staff, there are those who work equally hard behind the scenes to ensure that clients' needs are met.

I believe that the government recognises the contribution made by the independent sector and accepts that there is a need to work in partnership. Those who are opposed to this philosophy are in danger of taking the 'private versus public health care' debate back some 20 years.

St Augustine's in Stoke is one of the Cambian Group's 'state of the art' psychiatric rehabilitation independent hospitals.

All care homes need to receive realistic levels of fees in order to keep them viable. Recognition must be given to those who provide comprehensive staff training and development. Striving to provide a high standard of service and endeavouring to meet the National Minimum Standards is expensive.

These factors must be considered before one criticises the care industry. I believe one should speak up whenever articles or advertisements are published that could have a serious impact on the development of long-term care.

Reference

Ashurst, A. (2002) Defending independent care. *Nursing & Residential Care*, **4**(10), 465.

Mental health: Everyone's business

My first New Year's resolution is to encourage all *Nursing & Residential Care* (*NRC*) readers to help put mental health issues back into the media spotlight. In November 2005, the Department of Health launched a service development guide: *Everyone's Business: Integrated Mental Health Services for Older Adults*. Sims (2006) stated that

> The guide set out what it saw as the key components of a modern older people's mental health service, which includes providing users and carers with information on their condition and ensuring that they are consulted about care plans that are developed.

Older people with enduring mental health needs all deserve to be treated with respect. Their privacy and dignity must always be maintained.

Over the past decade, many large mental hospitals countrywide have closed their doors forever and the number of NHS psychiatric bed numbers have dramatically decreased. Older people with mental illnesses are now finding it almost impossible to manage on their own in the community and as a result they can become socially isolated, vulnerable and at risk of all types of abuse.

Care home owners, registered to care for older people with mental health needs, often accept people because there appears to be nowhere else for them to live. Without some form of rehabilitation, older people may become frustrated and there may be a serious exacerbation of their symptoms. How can we provide such individuals with the opportunity of improving their 'quality of life' within a care home environment?

Barchester Healthcare's 'Memory Lane' project has been a real success in managing older people with the effects of dementia. Having personally visited some of the 'Memory Lane' facilities, I was most impressed with the planners that provided older residents with open spaces and age-appropriate activities.

There are thousands of older people with mental health needs in care homes throughout the country and I believe that all care and therapy support staff that work in this specialist field of nursing and social care need to be provided with specialist training programmes in order to ensure that they are able to deliver a quality service.

All care homes should aspire to provide the highest levels of quality care, offering residents a supportive environment and, more importantly, the opportunity to benefit from a more productive future.

References

Ashurst, A. (2007) Everyone's business. *Nursing & Residential Care*, **9**(15).
Sims, B. (2006) Managing mental health. *Nursing & Residential Care*, **8**(1), 6.

Discussion points

- Older people with enduring mental health needs all deserve to be treated with respect. Their privacy and dignity must always be maintained. Why does this statement underpin our core values in nursing today?
- How can managers ensure that their staff will maintain high standards of care at all times?
- How can the night staff help in this important process?

Covert medication

The practice of nurses hiding drugs in food and drink was raised publicly by campaigner Hunter Watson, who discovered that staff in a Scottish care home had sedated his mother without consent, and had disguised drugs in her meals.

Mr Watson raised this serious issue with the Scottish Parliament. He told the BBC *News at Ten* (2 October 2007):

> It shouldn't happen. It is very convenient for staff at care homes to conceal drugs in the food and drink of residents, not for therapeutic problems but to make the residents easier to manage.

Covert medication and issues of consent have been debated by nurses and doctors for many years. The practice is often based on the judgment of a single nurse, and relatives may be kept in ignorance. This may be attributable to a culture of fear surrounding covert medication (Treloar *et al.*, 2000). However, today there are written guidelines for care home staff in Scotland stating that medication should be hidden in food or drink only when it is in the best interests of a resident, not for the convenience of staff. In England, the Commission for Social Care Inspection rules that staff may not administer medication covertly without the permission of a resident, the resident's family or representative if they are incapacitated, or a doctor who decides that unwanted medication is essential for their health and wellbeing.

A doctor or a pharmacist should also be consulted to check that crushing tablets to hide in food is safe.

At times some older people with dementia living in our care homes do need to receive their medication covertly. Care home managers hold the key to ensuring that if residents are to be given medicines in food and drink, then the correct communications with all those people involved in the decision making process are made. If residents continue to refuse to accept prescribed medication, a clinical review should be held. Discussions with the resident (if they are willing and able to partake) should be open and honest, and spell out the consequences. The decisions made and agreed on must be accurately recorded in the resident's care plan and doctor's notes. Nurses should never have to make a unilateral decision to hide any medication in a resident's food and drink without telling anyone. This climate of fear should be removed, wherever and whenever it occurs.

What is your view? Perhaps it is time for you to start putting your opinion forward. Nurses and health professionals must be given the opportunity to explain the circumstances that they face every day in a busy care home. In my experience, it has been necessary in certain circumstances to administer medication covertly, but only after the care home staff have followed the correct procedures and discussed their proposals with residents and relatives. We need to be sure that what we are doing in relation to drug administration is in the best interests of our residents, and we must always be accountable for our decisions.

References

Ashurst, A. (2007) Covert medication. *Nursing & Residential Care*, **9**(11), 501.
BBC News (2007) *News at Ten*, 2 October 2007.
Treloar, A., Beats, B. and Philpot, M. (2000) A pill in the sandwich: covert medication in food and drink. *Journal of the Royal Society of Medicine*, **93**, 408–11.

Who pays for wasting medicines?

At *Nursing & Residential Care* (*NRC*) we have always been prepared to speak out whenever we learn of issues that raise concerns among professionals working within the care industry. Today many General Practitioners (GPs) throughout the country are losing thousands of pounds per week. The problem is a simple one, involving the re-ordering of residents' medications.

Every month care homes are responsible for sending individual residents' repeat prescription requests to their local GP's surgery for the medicines required for the following 28 days.

The registered nurse highlights in writing those items not required on each individual resident's medication administration record (MAR) sheet. This is cross-referenced with the FP10 prescription which is signed by the GP.

It is much easier for GP surgery staff to re-order all medicines on the computerised list as they appear on the computer screen at the click of a mouse, rather than re-ordering each resident's medicines line by line.

Once the GP has signed off medications on the list, it is sent to the pharmacist and dispensed into blister packs or as individual bottles of liquids. Many GPs' surgery staff seemingly ignoring the care homes' specific instructions, leading to stock being dispensed that is neither needed nor used.

This waste appears to be endemic, and as a result GPs have to pay massive amounts of money out of their annual budgets to supply unwanted medicines to care homes.

Once the medicines have been dispensed from the pharmacist and delivered to the care home, they must be destroyed if they are not used.

If you suspect that your care home is carrying an excessive stock of certain medicines, you can address the issue by taking the following simple steps:

■ Initially an audit should be carried out to identify just how much stock is delivered to the care home that was not required. Findings should be recorded and published.

- The care home manager should then write to the GP and send a copy of the letter to the pharmacist highlighting the extent of the problem.
- At the end of 28 days the registered nurse should measure how much stock has remained unopened and therefore unused. Remember that all this stock is now wasted and the cost must be borne by someone.
- Care homes are willing to work in partnership with GPs and pharmacists. The GP's administration team and the pharmacist's team should all work together to promote a cost-effective and efficient system of ordering and dispensing of medications

Counting the cost of waste must be highlighted at some stage, and care homes have a 'duty of care' to speak up and expose areas of poor practice.

Reference

Ashurst, A. (2006) Who pays for wasting medicines? *Nursing & Residential Care*, **8**(9), 385.

Making mealtimes memorable

I am passionate about the care of older people and younger adults with a learning disability who live in residential care homes. I know from personal experience that throughout the country there are many care homes that produce and present well-balanced and nutritious meals for their residents.

I read with great interest the comments made by the Liberal Democrat MP Paul Burstow, when he said:

> Frail and vulnerable older people go into care homes to be cared for, not starved. It is shocking that today almost one in five care homes do not meet even the most basic of meal standards.

These comments made me angry because I believe they are based upon old data that gleaned from Commission for Social Care Inspection (CSCI) reports going back to 2004.

I would like to think that the care industry has moved on since then and that care home owners are now empowering their managers and chefs to produce meals of high quality within an agreed budget.

Do we really need a Jamie Oliver campaign to improve nutritional standards throughout the care industry?

The large corporate care providers can attract TV celebrity chefs to work with them and this initiative should be encouraged. However, we should not be relying upon one person, but should all take personal responsibility in each of our care homes.

There are thousands of small care home owners who find it difficult to survive with the continuing squeeze on their weekly fees, but older vulnerable people need to be given choices at mealtimes. There must be no excuse for chefs who constantly order expensive and unappetising frozen ingredients and as a result deliver meals without appearing to have any pride in their preparation or presentation.

Training catering staff is the answer. Barchester Healthcare, for example, has developed a catering academy designed to improve the skills of their chefs throughout the organisation. We should give CSCI inspectors the opportunity to sample residents' meals the next time they visit.

Monitor residents' feedback and encourage the chef to tour the dining room to see how the meals have been received. Monitor waste and eliminate convenience foods in favour of more home baking. Ensure that the dining room is an attractive place in which to serve people their meals. Remember that mealtimes are the highlight of some people's day. Ensure that your care home has plenty of fresh fruit and vegetables available so that the chef can produce dishes that are memorable rather than bland.

Finally, arranging special 'theme days' in the care home can be fun, offering meals from different countries. I'm sure that many overseas nurses would love to share their local recipes with the chef. I appreciate that older people prefer local dishes, but once in a while they may appreciate a change on the menu. If you do not try these ideas, you will never know the impact it could have!

Reference

Ashurst, A. (2006) Making mealtimes memorable. *Nursing & Residential Care*, **8**(3), 101.

Religion: a private matter?

Caroline Petrie, a qualified community bank nurse and devout Christian, hit the headlines after she was suspended from North Somerset Primary Care Trust after offering to pray for one of her older patients in the community.

Apparently a nursing colleague was informed about the prayer offer by the patient in passing the next day.

This sensitive case has raised many questions around religion and professional conduct and has implications for everyone involved in caring for others. There is a need for nurses and carers to be sensitive to other people's religious beliefs and customs. However, we live in a society where there is also a great deal of intolerance of, and in some cases ignorance about, certain religions.

Praying for others is most commendable, but in my opinion this should be carried out privately, without the need to seek the permission from the person for whom the nurse is offering their prayers. There are many ways of meeting the residents' spiritual needs without singling out specific residents.

In many successful care homes the residents' spiritual needs are often met by staff encouraging residents to practice their personal religious beliefs without fear or prejudice.

I recognise that nurses must acknowledge that the holistic needs of their residents are of paramount importance, and the Nursing and Midwifery Council (NMC) (2008) is clear in providing best practice guidance, stating:

Be open and honest, act with integrity and uphold the reputation of your profession: act with integrity; you must demonstrate a personal and professional commitment to equality and diversity.

Uphold the reputation of your profession: you must not use your professional status to promote causes that are not related to health.

A Department of Health (DoH) document, *Religion or Belief: A Practical Guide for the NHS*, stipulates that preaching or attempting to convert people at work 'can cause many problems, as non-religious people and those from other religions or beliefs could feel harassed and intimidated by this behaviour'.

The guide says that nurses should be allowed to wear religious dress, symbols and jewellery unless they conflict with health and safety procedure (DoH, 2009).

It is important that care home managers make themselves familiar with the contents of this important document.

Nurses do have a duty of care in all their dealings with residents and their families. However, the question remains: should our religious beliefs be shared with others while at work? I do not have the answers to this complex issue. I do, however, believe that religion should be kept separate from professional issues, and that there are valuable lessons to be learned by all parties on this issue.

I am pleased to note that Caroline Petrie the nurse at the centre of this political storm was offered her job back, due, in part, to massive media coverage and the groundswell of public opinion.

References

Ashurst, A. (2009) Religion: a private matter? *Nursing & Residential Care*, **11**(4), 169.

Department of Health (2009) *Religion or Belief: a Practical Guide for the NHS*. DoH, London.

Nursing and Midwifcry Council (NMC) (2008) *The Standards of Conduct, Performance, and Ethics for Nurses and Midwives*. NMC, London.

Discussion points

- How do your care home/hospital staff cater for the spiritual/cultural needs of your residents or patients?
- Do you provide a multi-faith room – a room that is provided for people to sit quietly and either pray or reflect upon their personal beliefs?
- Discuss the importance of meeting people's spiritual needs in a care setting.
- The manager has a very important responsibility to ensure that all residents' cultures are respected and valued.
- It is important to involve people's families to gain a better understanding of their religious beliefs.

CHAPTER 7

Building relationships

Working with outside agencies

As a care home manager it is essential that you have the ability to develop relationships with outside agencies. Some of these may include the local General Practitioners (GPs) and their team. It is important that the local surgery acknowledge the links with the care home.

GPs should have access to the care home in order to put in place a professional and respectful relationship. All residents have the right to see their GP and some visit the local surgery if possible. However, the GP may hold a weekly mini-surgery at the care home.

Communications between the care home and the surgery must include a positive response from the GP's receptionist whenever the staff request an essential GP visit.

The pharmacist

The care home manager needs to build good relationships with the local pharmacist in order to develop an excellent medication system that is both efficient and effective. Some large national pharmacy groups, such as Boots, offer care homes a dedicated bespoke service using the MDS system. However, smaller community pharmacists may also offer a bespoke service.

The suppliers

If the care home belongs to a large national care provider then choosing a food supplier may be outside the manager's remit. However, for those managers working for a sole provider there is a wonderful opportunity to find local approved suppliers. It is essential to get a competitive price on food supplied, but more importantly it is the reliability of service delivery, choice and quality products available that make the care home's and suppliers' relationships work well.

The suppliers of services including lift and general maintenance, fire safety and waste management. All must be very carefully chosen, as entering into long-term contracts can be expensive. The manager must monitor and audit all services provided to the care home and good two-way communications remains at the centre of building good relationships.

Working with local charities

Working in partnership with local charities can have mutual benefits for the care home and the chosen charity. For example, local charities, such as the Alzheimer's Society may be offered facilities within the care home to hold their monthly meetings. The benefit to the charity is that members of the Alzheimer's Society have an opportunity to meet the care home manager and staff and both parties can build positive and effective professional relationships. If vacancies occur in the care home then the charity's members may recommend the care home where they hold their meetings to their friends and relatives.

Assisting in local charities' fundraising efforts can have a major impact on the care home's relationship with them.

Volunteers may offer to provide a befriender service in the care home, since unfortunately some older residents do not have the pleasure of their relatives visiting as they may no longer live in the area.

Successfully handling complaints/relatives – partnership or confrontation?

The care home manager and their staff are responsible for the delivery of quality care and hotel services for residents on a daily basis. However, staff must also provide a quality service for every resident's family and friends whenever they visit their loved ones in the care home.

Successful care homes train all their staff members appropriately in all aspects of positive customer care, and in turn they endeavour to work closely with the residents' families.

It is not enough to give good service: customers must perceive that they are getting good service. The goal is not customer satisfaction but rather customer delight. Delight occurs when mistakes are openly acknowledged and rectified without argument and when customers are asked for feedback even before they have thought about complaining. The secret of turning customer service into a competitive advantage is to do something that makes you memorable and therefore different (Johns, 1994).

If the care home is recognised for being warm and friendly towards relatives, positive comments will be passed on by word of mouth, thus improving the care home's overall reputation. On the other hand, if care staff do not accommodate the needs of visitors and do not seek to work closely with families, then the reputation of the care home will be affected, as will occupancy and staff recruitment.

Relationships

Successful relationships between different groups of individuals are usually based upon several important factors:

- Feedback can be given both by staff and the family through face-to-face meetings and regular updates by email, telephone or letter.
- There must be a mutual trust and respect between all parties.
- Sometimes there may be a personality clash between two people and it is important that another staff member is allocated to the resident and their relatives to avoid any unnecessary friction developing in the care home.

Staff responsibilities

All staff working within care homes have a personal responsibility to provide high levels of quality care for residents and support for family members. Each member of the team should be seen as a valued individual with an important role to play in the delivery of care, whether it be from the care home manager or the chef.

The care home manager

The manager of the care home has overall responsibility for ensuring that the needs of the residents are met, but also that the needs of the relatives are anticipated and catered for.

How the manager deals with the many issues raised by the relatives will have a direct impact on the way that the overall care service is delivered within the home. Keeping everyone happy ensures that positive successful relationships can be developed and maintained and avoids the possibility of confrontation, which often occurs when family members are not involved in the decision-making process.

The nursing staff

Nursing staff work closely on a day-to-day basis with residents and their relatives and it is vital that they form good, trusting relationships with both. Working in partnership with the resident's family creates not only a network of support, but ensures that everyone's thoughts and needs are taken into consideration when making important decisions.

Nursing staff also have a number of special responsibilities, such as administering medication and supervising residents' meal times. In addition to writing care plans and ensuring that GP visits are well organised, staff must also be seen to support their junior colleagues in providing high-quality services.

The administrator

The administrator may deal with relatives' concerns that are of a non-clinical nature. They may have a query about an invoice or a hairdressing bill. The manner in which the administrator initially handles the relatives' concerns is critical, in order to ensure that concerns are dealt with speedily and efficiently and that the matter is resolved to everyone's satisfaction. Sadly, sometimes the matter needs to be taken further; the administrator will brief the manager and together they will attempt to resolve the issue amicably.

Treating relatives with respect and listening to their concerns is often enough to avoid confrontation.

The head chef

In any care home, food is often at the top of the agenda when it comes to relatives raising their concerns. There are some common complaints raised by relatives:

- Food may be presented poorly and the resident is expected to manage to cut up meat and vegetables without staff support.
- Food is cold when served and may be left out of the reach of the resident.
- The daily menu lacks nutritional balance and there is little or no choice offered.
- There is not enough fruit provided in the home and seldom do the residents have access to cold drinks during the day.
- At the week ends and during evening meals there appears to be a lack of choice with regard to hot food, as staff provide a variety of sandwiches as the second meal choice option.
- Residents seldom get offered any supper and the evening meal is served too early.
- There are no cooked breakfasts provided in the care home.

The head chef should try to get to know the residents and find out their individual likes and dislikes.

It is important that the head chef and their catering team provide choice and a nutritious balanced diet which is suitable for the age group and well presented.

The head chef plays a pivotal role in developing a balanced diet for all residents.

All complaints about the food must be reported to the head chef and these complaints are to be investigated robustly in order to prevent any re-occurrence and to ensure that standards are maintained in all areas of food hygiene, including the ordering, delivery, storage, preparation and presentation of food.

The housekeeper

A care home, independent hospital or community 'step-down' home that is kept clean and tidy will usually be free of odours. The housekeeper is responsible for making sure that his or her staff keep the home 'fit for purpose'.

Individual bedrooms are the focal point of a resident's life and therefore they need to be kept clean and tidy at all times.

When relatives are first shown around the home, they are taken to showrooms that are available for visitors to view. If the housekeeping team have failed to keep the rooms in good order, a potential resident may decide to go to another home.

Often residents and their relatives talk to the housekeeping staff, as they feel the care staff may be too busy. Therefore staff members need to be trained in the art of good verbal communication with both the residents and their families. If an issue is raised then the contents of the conversation must be passed on to the nurse in charge so that the matter can be dealt with quickly.

The care assistant/support worker

The care assistant/support worker is usually the person who talks most with the resident and their relatives and therefore needs to have the ability to deal with a variety of questions from relatives. Following these simple guidelines can help:

- Staff should take great pride in their appearance.
- Clean and tidy staff will always create a good impression with relatives.
- Staff need to adopt a professional approach to relatives. It is important for staff to learn people's names.
- Imagine arriving at a care home and being greeted by name – that's the first step to creating excellence in customer care.
- Complaints should be handled in a sensitive manner and properly investigated in order to show to all staff that the management are being seen to be fair.
- The staff need to be assured that the home's Complaints Policy and Procedure is designed and in place to ensure fairness to the residents, relatives and staff members.

- Often confrontation can be avoided if staff just take time out to listen carefully to the warning signs.

The domestic/laundry assistant

These staff members will come into daily contact with residents and relatives. Sometimes complaints are received concerning the laundry, and therefore staff must be trained in how to react when and if they are confronted with angry and upset relatives. Residents' laundry may go missing or get damaged and the home will have a policy on dealing with these matters.

It is important for the staff to alert the manager to any problems. Frustrations build up when relatives are not told the truth (for example regarding laundry that may have gone missing or been damaged in the washing process).

Communication

Communicating with the resident's family and keeping them involved and informed is vital when attempting to establish a pro-active relationship with others. The more they are kept in the information loop, the happier they will be. The manager should make themselves available to meet with relatives whenever they want to visit the home and a regular manager's surgery, held for a couple of hours, two evenings a week, often proves invaluable in helping to develop working partnerships between staff and relatives. Clear, concise information must be provided to relatives, and updates on the condition of the resident should be provided on at least a weekly basis. These updates can be made by email, telephone call or letter. A record must be kept of the date and time the message was given and to whom. This is very important if relatives come back at a later date and say they never heard from the staff of the home.

Creating a good working relationship between the resident's families, home manager and staff requires cooperation on both sides:

- Good open two-way communication between the resident's family members and staff is of paramount importance if there is to be a good continuous working relationship between both parties.
- Honesty from the manager and their staff to the residents and their families remains at the heart of this working relationship.
- Commitment should be demonstrated by care home staff that are prepared to go the 'extra mile' in order to ensure that the residents' needs are met in full.

- There should be a robust complaints procedure in place that allows people to complain about a service without fear of retribution from staff if they wish to complain.
- Transparency is an important factor, and family members should have access to the resident's care plan (with the resident's approval).
- Evidence-based 'best practice' must be delivered and outcomes measured. The positive results of which should be shared with the family at regular clinical reviews and one-to-one meetings with the manager.
- Meeting and exceeding expectations places the resident and their families at the centre of care rather than making them all feel like bystanders.
- Many relatives often feel guilty about placing their loved ones in a care setting, and this guilt may manifest itself in people becoming very quick to complain, rather than seeing that staff do sometimes make genuine mistakes.

Handling complaints

Effectively dealing with concerns, whether from residents or their relatives, is crucial in order to avoid confrontation. There are a number of factors which should be considered when addressing such issues:

- Any complaint should ideally be dealt initially within three working days and a full written response provided within a week if serious allegations have been made. In the latter case, the investigation may take longer, but the manager must explain this process to the relatives and keep them informed at all times.
- Staff must follow the home's Policies and Procedures to the letter whenever they are handling any complaint, no matter how small it appears at the time.
- Complaints can be very useful to the manager, as they may uncover bad practice which can be resolved only when the manager is made aware of an issue concerning relatives.
- Staff must be prepared for those who appear to complain about all aspects of care and the environment.
- Staff should seek relative's views about the quality of the service delivery, food and recreational activity programme. They should also be asked if they have any ideas for special events for the residents of the home.
- Staff attitude is important and everyone needs to be aware that speaking about the home, even when they are off duty, can get back to relatives.
- Confidentiality and a sensitive approach are of the utmost importance.

- Politeness and basic etiquette, like offering visitors a drink, takes only minutes of staff time but the rewards can be most worthwhile and will have a great impact on the overall reputation of the home.
- Simple guidelines are clear to follow. Staff should always pass on to their senior on duty any queries people may have as soon is practicable.
- Staff should never try to answer a question that they are unsure of, as relatives will always act upon information received from any source.

Conclusion

The reputation of any care home is dependent upon the way the staff work, either in partnership or confrontation with residents and their relatives. Relationships can often take time to develop, but if staff put the resident at the centre of all they do, then relatives should accept that at times there may be issues that they are not satisfied with, but which can be solved and dealt with amicably if good relationships are maintained.

Care home managers that operate an 'open-door policy' and arrange to communicate regularly with residents and their relatives are able to resolve most issues through open and frank discussion, rather than having to take a reactive stance to any issues raised. This makes for a setting in which all those involved in providing and receiving care work in partnership with one another (Johns, 1994).

References:

Ashurst, A. (2006) Working with families – partnership or confrontation? *Nursing & Residential Care*, **8**(11), 508–11.

Johns, T. (1994) *Perfect Customer Care*, p. 47. Random House, London.

Key points

- There must be a mutual trust and respect between the residents' families, the care home manager and staff.
- Transparency is evident when family members, with the resident's approval, are given access to the care plan and involved in the decision-making process.

> ■ Complaints should be handled in a sensitive manner and properly investigated in order to show all staff that the management are being seen to be fair.
>
> ■ The staff need to be assured that the home's Complaints Policy and Procedure is designed and in place to ensure fairness to the resident, their relatives and staff.

Providing support for relatives

Alzheimer's disease was subject of a television documentary: the *One Life* special 'Mum and Me' was transmitted by the BBC on 17 May 2008.

I watched the programme with great interest, as the complexities of the relationship unfolded between Sue Bourne, a documentary film producer and director, and her mother Ethel, an Alzheimer's sufferer in her eighties and living in a care home in Ayr, Scotland. The documentary managed to capture Ethel's brilliant sense of humour, retained despite her suffering the devastating effects of Alzheimer's. The special bond between Sue and her mother was also shown, highlighting some of the difficulties experienced in a mother and daughter relationship. Sue visited her mother at least once a month.

This involved an 800 mile round car trip between London and Scotland. During the filming, Sue suffered from cancer but she managed to keep this news from her mother. I did find some of the dialogue within this documentary uncomfortable, as Sue eventually appeared on one occasion to lose her temper with her mother. But I do admire her for keeping this piece of material in the documentary when the easy solution would have been to edit out the unpleasant scene.

I believe that care home managers and staff must recognise and act upon the fact that they all have a duty of care to support and educate relatives who may find visiting a parent with Alzheimer's a distressing experience. We should share best practice and work with relatives in developing a care plan that not only meets the needs of the older person but also identifies the relative's needs. 'Mum and Me' evoked a great deal of public comment; many viewers found the film inspirational, reminding them of their own family's situation; however, one viewer asked 'was Ethel capable of giving consent to this? If not, then whatever the merits are, then this should not have been on TV'.

In 2007 Paul Watson produced a brilliant film 'Love's Farewell' featuring Barbara and Malcolm Pointon, and I believe that this documentary has had a major impact upon the way many people view Alzheimer's and its devastating consequences.

Watching 'Mum and Me' has highlighted once again the important and pivotal role that relatives play in the continuing care of their parents.

Relatives and staff should be encouraged to contact The Alzheimer's Society, the leading care and research charity for people with all forms of dementia and their carers. It provides information and education, support for carers, and quality day and home care.

The Society's national help line is 0845 300 0336 and their website is http://www.alzheimers.org.uk/.

With dignity in care also being at the media's forefront, the Alzheimer's Society's chief executive, Neil Hunt, has announced

It is encouraging to see the government wants dignity at the heart of the new NHS constitution, supported by a national awareness campaign. There are 700 000 people living with dementia in the UK and if we live past 65 years old one in three of us will die with dementia. Dignity and quality of care is key to supporting those affected and needs to be considered in the country's first ever National Dementia Strategy due out later this year.

References

Ashurst, A. (2008) Providing support for relatives. *Nursing & Residential Care*, **10**(7), 318.

Bourne, S. (2008) *One Life* series 'Mum and Me'. BBC TV, 17 May.

Discussion points

■ How can the care home manager and her team improve their links with local charities?
■ What steps can be taken to improve relatives' visiting times at care homes?

CHAPTER 8

Refurbishment projects

Successful residential refurbishment

Perhaps one of the most interesting aspects of care home management is to participate in and facilitate a refurbishment project.

Larger projects may involve internal re-building works and a great deal of disruption to the day-to-day running of the care home.

The successful refurbishment must be carried out within a specific agreed time frame and be completed under budget if at all possible.

In providing a step-by-step guide I am keen to point out that every project is only as successful as the people that are involved in all aspects of the scheme.

Both the management and the staff must project a positive attitude to ensure full cooperation with contractors and decorators to prevent any disruption to plans.

Whatever the reason the following principles of good practice should be adhered to in an endeavour to prevent the project being over budget and poorly managed.

■ Choose contractors that are sympathetic to working in care settings and have experience in this type of work.
■ Ensure you communicate with all interested parties in writing, keeping them informed of progress.
■ Spend time planning, and when the plan/programme is agreed, monitor the work to ensure that the schedule is being followed.
■ No additional work is to be carried out without authorisation.
■ Use experts only if you have money in your budget to meet their fees.
■ Ask residents what furniture and carpets they would prefer.
■ Involve staff in all aspects of refurbishment, as disruptions will be lessened if they are kept up to date with schedule.
■ When the work is finished throw a party for all and enjoy the long-term benefits, which should be significant if the job has been well done.
■ Remember to have a 'snags list' of any items outstanding.

Planning

It is important to draw up concise plans for the project. If these plans involve any change of usage to the nursing/residential facilities, a copy should be forwarded to the registration department for their approval. The fire officer may also wish to discuss any new plans if they involve any physical changes to the building.

A check must also be made to see if the building is listed in any way.

Once the plans have been drawn up they should be fully costed. Include everything that you can possibly think of, because once the budget has been agreed it is not easy to go back and request more money due to an oversight in the original plans.

- If outside builders/decorators have been authorised to carry out the work it is important that they produce written evidence of public liability insurance before they are allowed on the premises.
- Prior to the commencement of work ensure that a timed programme has been agreed in writing.
- No additional work must be authorised unless agreed with the project manager (usually a home manager or the owner).
- As a precaution it is advisable to check that the nurse call system, fire alarm system and telephone system are all in good working order prior to the commencement of any refurbishment programme. There may be the possibility of contractors accidentally damaging some or all of these systems. Liability can then be established.

Furniture that may be required

Depending on the client group within your home (e.g. frail and elderly clients or clients with physical disabilities) you may choose to buy new furniture for the lounge and dining areas.

When buying chairs many suppliers will offer good discounts if all chairs are purchased at one time. It is useful to shop around to ensure that any chairs are suitable for the purpose. Often people buy new chairs and then discover they are totally unsuitable for the clients.

All chairs should be covered in a material that allows regular cleaning and retains a modern, comfortable appearance. They should be fire retardant and meet with British Safety Standards – always look for the kite mark.

Be certain to check delivery times with suppliers, as sometimes chairs need to be ordered at least six to eight weeks in advance.

Ensure that the lounge carpet is suitable for industrial use, not simply domestic use, as excessive use could fade a simple domestic carpet very quickly.

Decoration

I would recommend that you get advice and support from professional decorators. Usually these quotes will give a clear picture of the best 'value for money' option. Often residents are encouraged to participate in the choice of wallpaper and colours. As there are thousands of colour schemes and wallpaper books available, the professional decorator can advise on what materials are available at a reasonable price.

Dining room

Tables need to be large enough to accommodate wheelchairs and yet small enough to appear homely. In addition, it is advisable to buy dining chairs with arms, as these can assist the clients' posture and balance, helping them to retain their dignity when sitting at the table. Chairs should be fitted with 'skids' which enable movement without danger to the client or carers. Ensure that you check the brochures for the right specification. As with the lounge furniture, check that the chairs can be easily cleaned.

Pictures

Whenever a refurbishment takes place it is reasonable to buy some new pictures for all areas. There are specialist artists' outlets that can offer framed contemporary prints at a reasonable price. Pictures help to brighten up the home and residents' input should be adhered to.

Bedrooms

When refurbishing bedrooms it is important to choose beds which are 'fit for purpose' and while many high street stores offer a range of cheap beds, these may not last. It is therefore always advisable to place your order with a recognised dealer.

The bed design can vary from adjustable hospital-type beds at the top of the range to simple divan beds. The client group should be considered and beds chosen to best suit their needs. For example, do you need a bed that has an adjustable height facility? This is most useful for the elderly or disabled client who needs to have a hoist in their room for all transfers.

Bedroom furniture includes wardrobes and dressing tables with chairs. These items are essential to give the bedroom a personalised, homely touch.

Cheap furniture may be easily damaged if you are dealing with a young challenging client group. Extra money spent on quality mattresses and furniture when costing up the original specification may save lots of replacements in the future.

Once again suppliers are often happy to offer discounts when they deliver large quantities of furniture at a time. Remember to check that delivery dates fit in with your prearranged timetable, as you do not want to have 20 wardrobes blocking the rest of the care home if your scheme has not been completed.

Bathrooms

Today many clients prefer to shower, but you must ensure that any showers fitted are drained and accessible to wheelchair users.

Does the bathroom have adequate wheelchair turning points?

Are the doors wide enough?

A normal bath also needs to be positioned with good access for mechanical hoists and for staff who may be required to assist with clients' bathing.

Bathrooms and *en suite* facilities need to be well ventilated and decorated in a functional but homely manner. Flooring for both these areas needs to be specialised and fitted by experts. Ensure that flooring is sealed well and any tiles are well grouted to avoid dampness at a later date.

All sinks/showers/baths must be fitted with thermostatically controlled valves to prevent clients and staff scalding themselves.

Fire alarms

Following any refurbishment, you need to ensure that all areas are linked into the existing fire alarm system, this includes automatic door closers. It is advisable to ask your fire maintenance contractor to deal with this issue, as they know the home and its current fire alarm system installation.

Communications

It is essential that all staff, residents and relatives are informed of the plans for any refurbishment programme. They also need to be informed when the work will be carried out.

There will inevitably be some noise and a certain amount of disruption, but this should be kept to a minimum.

Good communication between contractors and staff is important, as permission and reasonable notice must be given to carry out certain procedures, such as turning off the care home's water supply.

Ensure that staff prepare for refurbishment by adequately clearing out areas concerned.

If contractors arrive and rooms are still full of residents' personal property this can delay progress and cause poor working relationships to develop.

During the works

Ensure that areas are sealed off to reduce dust, noise and general disturbance.

Move residents to a suitable area during the refurbishment. This relocation needs to be discussed, especially as elderly clients are often reluctant to vacate their rooms.

Signs must be placed to alert people visiting the home that work is taking place, to avoid potential accidents.

Any skips/lorries and delivery of materials should be confined to a designated area and be the sole responsibility of the contractors. Building supplies are often the target of thieves. Maintaining security is therefore vital.

If the heating system is cut off, ensure that an adequate alternative supply has been put in place. It is advisable to carry out works in the summer months.

Completion

Upon completion, before signing off the works always draw up a 'snags list'. This details small areas that may need finishing off. When these works have been carried out to your satisfaction the refurbishment is complete.

The registration/fire officer may wish to visit to check that the work matches the original plans.

Within your care home a refurbishment programme may be carried out for a variety of reasons which include the following:

- To improve the general decoration of the building
- To improve the occupancy and take the home 'up market'
- To meet registration inspection requirements
- To extend present services by developing better facilities

During any refurbishment programme it is important to maintain the high standards of care for the residents.

Reference

Ashurst, A. (1999) Successful residential refurbishment. *Nursing & Residential Care*, **1**(8), 466–70.

Key points

- Time spent planning a refurbishment is critical to its ultimate success.
- The 'project manager' must be responsible and accountable for all work carried out and meet the budget set.
- Ensure that clients and staff are involved in choosing colours and pictures.
- All outside contractors must have evidence of public liability insurance before commencing any work in the care home.
- Work should cause minimum disruption to existing residents.

Discussion points

- How would you ensure that residents and their families are informed of any refurbishment plans for the care home?
- How would you ensure that your residents have a say in the colour schemes for the refurbishment programme?
- Describe the importance of a 'snags list' and how would you ensure these issues are resolved.

Working with architects and building contractors

As a care home manager you may one day, if your care home is going to undertake an extension to your existing facility, have the opportunity to work alongside architects and interior designers.

Architects are professional people who are commissioned to provide care home owners with detailed plans that describe in minute detail the plans which will be handed to the builders, who will follow the plans and eventually build the care home's new premises.

It is important that care home owners agree the plans before building work commences. It is vitally important to ensure that the architects and builders work closely together through out the whole project. Any changes are requested to the original plans once the building work has commenced will inevitably lead to increased costs, not only in materials but also in time.

Architects with experience in building care homes have developed 'state of the art' buildings which are 'fit for purpose', allowing residents much more space and wider corridors, with *en suite* rooms that have modern bathroom suites in place. Residents' requirements in the future may include the introduction of gyms and access to Internet and phones, plus multi-channel digital television with Freeview or satellite TV channels.

Successful care home managers must continue to work closely with architects and builders in order to achieve the satisfactory completion of both extensions and any new builds in place.

Building contractors

The responsibility of transferring the detailed plans designed by the architect remains with the building contractors. The building site can be very dangerous and therefore needs to be protected 24 hours a day and seven days a week.

The builders work closely with the architect and the client by holding regular site meetings. Any alterations requested by the client can be very expensive, and as the project continues it is very important that the client is very involved in the overall success of the vision.

As a care home manager it is important to understand how building projects are put together, so as part of your personal development it is advisable to get to know the architect and the site foreman who can explain the development in an easy 'step-by-step' approach.

Therefore if your employer asks what stage the project has reached at any time you can answer with a better understanding than if you have no idea of the process.

The development of Delfryn Lodge in Mold, North Wales.

All building projects are different, but given the opportunities you have to be involved it is important that you take them and learn. Remember that nothing can replace your personal experience.

The interior designer plays a very important part in completing the new building before residents take up their new accommodation. The importance of showcasing original large, appropriate photographs and art work has been

A well-designed kitchen for patients undertaking intensive psychiatric rehabilitation.

recognised as making a great impact when promoting the overall ambience of the facility.

CHAPTER 9

Health and safety in the care home

Health and safety in the care home

Care home owners and their managers are responsible for protecting residents, relatives, visitors and staff, and for keeping them informed about any health and safety issues as and when they occur.

Accidents and incidents can happen in a busy care home at any time of day or night. Accurate factual reports of any incident must be written up as soon as is practical and countersigned by the nurse in charge or the care home manager. Staff should be reminded never to listen to hearsay or write down someone else's version of events following an accident or incident.

The manager will be responsible for ensuring that all accident and incident forms are completed correctly.

Completing an accident report.

Ashurst (2007) goes on to say:

The robust investigation process if carried out in a professional manner can often reveal the causes and consequences and identify those responsible.

Kirby and Maher (2004) suggest that:

Falls are a common problem in the older population for those in care homes, bringing with them increased mortality, personal suffering and health care costs. Roughly 50% of care home residents fall each year. The risk of falls increases with age, hence the number of incidents can be expected to increase as our population increases.

However, the risk of serious falls represents just one aspect of the health and safety dilemmas that are present in a care home setting. Therefore it is imperative that care home managers ensure that residents, relatives, visitors and their staff are kept in a safe environment.

Every employer has a duty under the law to ensure that, as far as is reasonably practicable, staff members' health, safety and welfare are maintained whilst they are at work. The care home manager, on behalf of the employer, must consult staff safety representatives on any matters relating to health and safety at work, including:

- Any changes that may substantially affect the health and safety at work, e.g. in procedures, using equipment or methods of working, policies and procedures. Action plans must be implemented following the completion of risk assessments.
- The appointment of a lead person who has a commitment to walk through the care home and identify any H&S issues. The daily walk through needs to be recorded. The manager must be kept fully informed of any outstanding issues on a daily basis.

Establishing a safe environment

In order to maintain a safe working environment staff need to be fully trained in health and safety.

One of the most important pieces of machinery in the care home is the lift system. The lift control room must be kept locked and only accessed by authorised personnel. The plant and boiler room must also be kept locked and free of rubbish.

The lift needs to be kept in good working order and be regularly serviced by professional lift service engineers. Staff must report any issues relating to the lift to the care home manager as soon as they occur. A detailed record must be kept of any call-outs to the lift engineering company. Usually the lift engineers will provide the care home staff with an explanation of what was wrong and what they did to put the problem right.

All equipment should be fit for purpose and any faults must be reported to the care home manager immediately. A note must be made, with the date that the faulty or broken equipment was reported and the nature of the problem. All equipment should be covered by a service contract.

Staff should always be provided with appropriate protective clothing and eye protection when necessary.

Staff should be made aware of all safety signs and fire exits and equipment and should ensure that the corridors and stairwells are kept free of any obstructions.

The care home should be maintained at a reasonable and a constant comfortable room temperature.

In forward-thinking care homes, the residents are now encouraged to use the Internet to stay in touch with their family and friends. It is useful to provide simple training for staff and residents in the use of computers and as long as the policies and procedures are followed then the care home can benefit from being linked to the community via the Internet.

Staff training

Staff must be trained in first aid at work and certain staff are nominated each day to be responsible for any first aid that needs to be carried out during their shift. The first aiders' names must be displayed in the care home. Appropriate first aid facilities and equipment must be provided. The health and safety consequences of introducing new technology must be addressed. Those using new computers, for example, should be advised on reducing the risk of associated hazards, such as repetitive strain injury of the wrist and visual or posture problems.

Making the workplace safe

The home manager and staff are responsible for ensuring that the care home is kept clean and tidy and that all corridors, stairwells and public areas are kept free from hazards or obstructions. The home environment is extremely important with respect to the care of vulnerable people.

It is important for staff to check residents' rooms to ensure that any electrical appliances are portable appliance tested (PAT) and are working correctly. The home maintenance person, who should have received accredited PAT testing training, can carry out this important duty through the home. The workplace should be well ventilated, kept at a comfortable temperature and have appropriate lighting, especially in corridors. Sanitary, washing and proper rest facilities for staff should be provided.

What Health & Safety Executive inspectors can do

Health & Safety Executive (HSE) inspectors are required by law to inspect care homes to ensure that health and safety laws are being kept. The HSE inspectors have the powers to:

- Stop any dangerous activity
- Force the home to remedy an unsatisfactory or unsafe situation with a certain amount of time
- Prosecute the organisation and/or line manger personally if they do not follow health and safety laws, despite being warned
- Prosecute any employee who intentionally disobeys health and safety law
- Prosecute a home owner or manager who does not provide and maintain emergency and health and safety equipment, as required by law
- Close a care home if they believe it is necessary as a last resort

Ensuring that plant and machinery are safe

When carrying out a care home's health and safety audit, the manager must ensure that the plant/boiler room is kept free from any debris. Lifts can prove to be troublesome if they are not strictly maintained and professionally serviced. Staff must be ready to report any faults immediately to their manager.

Does the lift room have rubber matting in place to isolate from the risk of electric shock? It is most important to check that the lift room is always kept locked. All machinery and equipment should be fit for purpose and correctly maintained and serviced in line with the manufacturer's guidelines. Staff should be freely provided with the appropriate protective clothing and equipment to carry out their duties safely. Appropriate safety signs must be displayed and maintained throughout the home, including fire exits and equipment.

Moving and storing

The Health & Safety Executive guidelines entitled *The Control of Substances Hazardous to Health Regulations* (1999) (COSHH) must be followed when moving articles and substances around the home. Substances must be stored and used safely. Chemicals which are used for cleaning throughout the home must not only be stored safely but must be used correctly. If chemicals are not stored safely, then they could have fatal consequences.

Hawkins and Ashurst (2006) state that:

> The COSHH guidelines state that employers must stop or control the exposure of staff to hazardous substances such as dust, fumes and chemicals or bacteria and viruses causing cross-infection.

These regulations cover:

■ Cleaning materials (e.g. disinfectants), including a COSHH file which says what, where and how hazardous substances should be stored and moved
■ Dealing with clinical waste, which is defined as all waste that has been in contact with blood or other bodily fluids
■ Spillage of either chemicals or body fluids
■ Providing staff with adequate welfare facilities in the home
■ Staff must be reassured that their personal welfare is of paramount importance

The successful manager recognises that looking after their staff's health and safety will often result in a happier staff group. Managers should be aware of stress levels, and ensure that staff sickness records are monitored. If staff are suffering from stress and require some form of assistance, this must be addressed with great sensitivity. Excellent staff training in health and safety remains at the centre of any successful care home. If a manager provides up-to-date information and instruction relating to health and safety, this will inevitably go a long way in improving staff and public safety. There may also be a marked reduction in the level of accidents and ill health involving staff. Employees also have important legal duties:

- They should take reasonable care of their own health and safety and that of others who may be affected by their actions.
- Cooperating with one's employer on health and safety.
- Correctly using work items provided by an employer, including personal protective equipment in accordance with training or instructions.
- Not interfering with or misusing anything provided for health, safety or welfare purposes.
- Safe practice must also be demonstrated to the HSE in the event of an audit, the enforcing authority on standards.

Conclusions

Care home managers must take health and safety very seriously and should compile and provide a set of policies and procedures for their staff to follow. These policies should be read and signed by staff to demonstrate that they have read and understood the contents of the individual policies. Any instructions should be regularly updated and passed on to staff via regular training sessions.

There are many issues that can arise, from a resident's fall to an outbreak of fire in the home. Staff must also accept and carry out their personal responsibilities concerning health and safety issues. Ultimately, however, the manager must accept personal responsibility for all actions that are taken by their staff.

Health and safety audits and the resulting documentation are extremely important. It is necessary to clearly outline an action plan following the audit, providing details of which staff are responsible for correcting any outstanding issues. Health and safety documentation must be carried out diligently and should be checked daily. It is important for home managers to remind their staff that health and safety remain everyone's individual responsibility. If health and safety are not taken seriously this may result in a visit from the HSE, the possibility of prosecution and ultimately the closure of the home. To prevent such serious consequences, all managers need to put health and safety high on their list of priorities, so that residents, relatives, visitors and staff benefit in the long term.

Health and safety: further information

The Health and Safety Executive
Our mission is to prevent death, injury and ill-health in Great Britain's workplaces

We do this through research, information and advice, promoting training, new or revised regulations and codes of practice, inspection, investigation and enforcement (HSE website; accessed 20 March 2009).

HSE Info line: 0845 345 0055
Access to information, advice and support

Info line is the HSE's public enquiry contact centre. It provides access to workplace health and safety information, guidance and expert advice.

Website: http://www.hse.gov.uk/aboutus/ (accessed 20 March 2009)

Key points

■ Employers have a duty, under the law, to ensure, as far as is practicable, that the health, safety and welfare of staff is maintained at work.

■ Staff should take reasonable care of their own health and safety, and that of others who may be affected by their actions.

■ Excellent staff training in health and safety remains at the centre of a successful care home.

■ Health and safety documentation must be carried out diligently and should be checked daily.

CHAPTER 10

Sharing best practice

Are we doing enough?

More than half of nurses on mental health wards have reported being physically assaulted at work. The findings were published in February 2008 in the national audit of violence in mental health services, conducted on behalf of the Healthcare Commission by the Royal College of Psychiatrists (RC Psych).

The audit highlighted the high levels of violence on mental health wards, and stated that the impact on staff and patient can be 'constant and intolerable'. It was acknowledged that improvements had been made to the way violence is managed on wards for people of working age, particularly in providing effective alarm systems, reporting incidents and having an appropriate mix of skills among the staff team. Dr Paul Lelliott from the RC Psych commented that

> those working on psychiatric wards, and in particular the nurses, are the unsung heroes of mental health care. Their every working day is a challenge and this audit once again highlights the danger to their personal safety. Despite this, ward staff continue to provide care to the most severely ill people in a professional and compassionate manner.
>
> We have learnt over the past five years that good leadership is the single most important ingredient for quality and safety. Mental health services must give ward managers the authority to manage their wards effectively and must ensure that they have the resources they need to create as safe an environment as possible.

Anna Walker, Chief Executive of the Healthcare Commission, said

> this audit is a testament to the commitment and compassion of nurses that such a high number of patients in their wards says they are treated with dignity and respect.

Some of the issues raised in the national audit may be found in care home settings and the recommendations outlined should be implemented to reduce the risk of dedicated care staff suffering assault from older residents in their care. Some of the recommendations outlined in the audit included:

■ Care home managers need to address the problem of residents with functional disorders sharing communal areas with residents who have organic disorders.
■ Care home staff should do more to reduce avoidable noise.
■ Staff should review their provision of therapies and activities, particularly during evenings and weekends.
■ The care team need to assess whether measures can be taken to reduce confusion and anxiety caused by the layout of the care home, for example, by using pictures, colour coding or signage.
■ Review the training and support provided that relates to preventing and managing violent behaviour. Managing violence and aggression training is necessary for those staff working with older people with dementia.
■ The manager and head of care need to review whether incident reporting systems are adequate.

Staff will always remain the most valued asset within any care home. However, care home managers must recognise any shortfalls within their establishment and implement ways of improving staff safety at work.

Recommendations are easy to make and make lots of sense, but if they are never implemented the sole purpose of the academic exercise may be lost forever.

No one working in the care sector can afford to be complacent regarding staff safety.

References

Ashurst, A. (2008) Are we doing enough? *Nursing & Residential Care*, **10**(9), 422.
Healthcare Commission and the Royal College of Psychiatrists (2008) *National Audit of Violence (NAV)*.

Leadership, motivation and support

It is acknowledged that many leaders do not have empathy, but it is observed that those who lack empathy lack the ability to move people.

Leaders who can instil an atmosphere of working together gain respect, taking charge without taking control (Bennis, 1994).

Developing your leadership skills

Good managers often demonstrate the ability to lead their teams successfully in many walks of life. Football managers inspire their players to believe in themselves and beat the opposition. Football is all about confidence within the team. There are many examples of teams that have survived relegation against the odds.

Excellent care home managers appear to possess the same skills as football managers, in that they often exceed their staff's expectations.

In my view one of the secrets of their success is often found in the manner in which they lead their team members.

Excellent leaders in a care environment spend lots of time to develop their team to possess a consistent approach to caring and supporting the residents.

It is important to set a good example to your staff by knowing your residents and their families.

By appointing the right people into the key roles within your team, you will be able to depend upon your staff to deliver the high standards of care and service that you need to ensure that your care home is profitable and enjoys a great reputation.

- You need to be seen to be *dependable* in being there for people when they need your support. This includes dealing with concerns from residents, families and staff alike.
- You need to be *reliable* in your management of the care home. Being a care home manager is no longer a forty hour week. Managers need to be available for advice even if they are off duty.
- Care home managers need to be *strong* in their resolve to implement some very tough decisions at times, especially in difficult economic conditions.
- One of the most important attributes of any care home manager's role is that they must be *trustworthy*. It is essential that they are able to manage their budgets and oversee residents' monies in an efficient manner.
- The care home managers must be seen to be *loyal* to the company they work for. Sometimes companies have to make unpopular decisions and if managers are seen to be disloyal this action can be seen to be disloyal to the company. This may subsequently have a serious damaging effect on the company's reputation.

- Excellent managers should be *motivational* and *inspirational*, always endeavouring to provide their staff with opportunities to maximise their personal potential.
- Great managers must be *dedicated* to improving their care home's performance.
- Effective care home managers must be *accountable* for all their actions both at work and off duty. They are accountable to their employers and funders – purchasers of care and the Care Quality Commission.
- To be a great leader it is essential to show empathy to your staff. You must be able to relate to their personal situation and provide staff with solutions to their circumstances. As a parent I can empathise with staff who need to request time off from work to attend their children's sports day, but before I became a parent I did not have the same sort of insight into the staff's needs.

Recognising motivational techniques

Motivating people who work for you requires special skills, including the ability to inspire, enthuse, encourage those around you to go the extra mile for their residents.

Inspiration

Have you ever been inspired to undertake something you never thought you could achieve?

I once attended a company team-building exercise and was amazed to see how people could be inspired to undertake the frightening task of abseiling down a 35 feet castle wall. Even people who don't like heights seemed to be inspired to undertake the abseil. It was interesting to hear people say that they wanted to do it again having overcome their initial fear.

In order to inspire people you need to be able to communicate your plan and ensure that individuals 'buy in' to your ideas. Everyone possesses individual strengths and you can use these strengths to improve your team's overall performance. It is important to recognise that you get the best out of people by involving them fully in the planning and implementation of your plans. People are often too resistant to change because their leaders and managers are not inspirational in their management approach.

Staff enjoying the Cambian Group football and netball tournaments at Lilleshall – the home of Sport England – July 2009.

Annual sports day

At the Cambian Group we arrange an annual sports day for all staff to participate in. There are football and netball tournaments and afterwards there is a special meal and awards are presented.

This special social event has now become part of the Cambian calendar and provides staff with the opportunity to meet in an informal setting and inspire each other.

Enthusiasm

If you are enthusiastic about your role at work then your enthusiasm will become infectious amongst your team members.

Enjoying working with care staff and residents can sometimes be very challenging, but being enthusiastic is one special way of motivating others.

Great managers should always emphasise the positives rather than be negative in nature.

Optimism is much preferred to pessimism, which can have a detrimental effect on staff morale.

Encouragement

Encouraging your staff to perform well is essential to making staff feel valued in the workplace. Your encouragement of staff can make a real difference. One of the best ways of encouraging your staff is to 'walk the floor', reviewing staff performance. It is a great idea to talk to your residents, relatives and staff members at least one hour a day. Listen carefully to what's actually being said about your care home's service delivery. Encouragement of staff may include the introduction of initiatives like 'Employee of the Month'; the staff incentive scheme can often be seen in some hotels and supermarkets. Recognising staff who have exceeded customers' expectations can encourage staff to work in a more productive and satisfying way.

Reference

Bennis, W. (1994) *On Becoming a Leader*, 2nd edn. Basic Books, New York.

Key points

- Excellent managers should be **motivational** and **inspirational**, always endeavouring to provide their staff with opportunities to maximise their personal potential.
- Care home managers need to be **strong** in their resolve to at times implement some very tough decisions, especially in these difficult economic times of recession.
- Encouragement of staff may include the introduction of initiatives like 'Employee of the Month'; the staff incentive scheme can often be seen in some hotels and supermarkets.

Discussion points

- Describe some of the skills managers require in order to motivate their staff team.

- What incentives can you introduce to improve staff attendance and effectiveness in the care home?
- Which group of people are the managers accountable to within a care home?

Preventing the spread of infection

[*Note*: this section was written as the swine flu pandemic developed. Updated information follows below.]

After the outbreak of the influenza A H1N1 virus – known as swine flu – in Mexico several months ago, there was intensive media coverage as new cases were reported and confirmed in countries across the world.

Then, after a few weeks, the news agenda moved on to other important subjects. This does not mean, however, that the risk has disappeared.

I believe that all managers and staff working in care homes need to find out as much as they can about the spread, treatment and effects of swine flu and familiarise themselves with the care home's contingency plan, outlining the management arrangements in place should your care home experience an outbreak of swine flu.

The UK is likely to be struck by a swine flu pandemic in the early autumn, according to John Oxford, an influenza expert and professor of virology at St Bartholomew's and the Royal London Hospital (Batty, 2009).

The Government has taken the threat of a possible pandemic very seriously, producing a series of television and written media advertisements, plus a nationwide leafleting campaign.

Every household in the country was targeted to alert people to the signs and symptoms of swine flu and the treatments available.

At the time of writing the World Health Organization had confirmed that swine flu had spread to more than 66 countries with more than 18,965 confirmed cases worldwide. There have so far been 125 deaths reported; 80% of these have been in Mexico, with deaths also in Canada, USA, Chile and Costa Rica.

The number of confirmed cases of swine flu in the UK passed 557 on 8 June, with more cases being investigated.

The UK has taken a crucial step towards producing a swine flu vaccine. A strain of the swine flu virus suitable for making a vaccine has been produced and is being made available to flu laboratories around the world and to the pharmaceutical industry so that they can begin the first steps in the vaccine production process (Directgov, 2009).

Managers and staff do need to recognise the importance of preventing the spread of infection both inside and outside of their place of work. The number of cases reported in the UK is rising on a daily basis so we must all do our part to prevent the spread of the virus. Flu viruses can remain on surfaces for a long time and there may be serious implications for the local community if healthcare staff leave work and go straight out shopping, for example, while they are still wearing their uniform.

Next time you visit your local supermarket you may be surprised at the number of staff wearing their uniforms in public places.

Complacency is not an option for those working in nursing and residential care, as we continue to protect our vulnerable residents and their families. We must be diligent in our fight against swine flu.

References

Ashurst, A. (2009) Preventing the spread of infection. *Nursing & Residential Care*, **11**(7), 326.

Batty, D. (2009) Expert warns of autumn swine flu pandemic. *The Guardian*, 1 June, p. 7.

Directgov (2009) Swine flu – everything you need to know. http://www.direct.gov. uk/swineflu/; accessed 8 June 2009.

It is interesting to note that since the above was written the Health Protection Agency estimates there have been 668,000 cases of swine flu in the UK.

Hospitals were put on alert to expect a resurgence of the pandemic during the winter.

A vaccine was produced and is freely available to those people who are considered at risk due to underlying existing medical conditions. In addition, front line health care workers were also offered the vaccine . The Government set up a swine flu information hot line.

The majority of swine flu sufferers appear only to have had a minor short-term illness, but lessons were learned for the management of future pandemics affecting the country as a whole.

The Government was proactive in communicating with people concerning the signs and symptoms of swine flu, but it is worth noting that seasonal flu still claims vulnerable adults each year.

We all have a responsibility to ensure that we heed medical advice, and if staff need to be off duty we must have a contingency plan in place to back fill the spaces left on the duty rota.

The box shows the information made available to the public via the Internet.

National Pandemic Flu Service

If you are in England and feel like you may have swine flu, visit the National Pandemic Flu Service by following the link below, or call 0800 1 513 100 (text phone – 0800 1 513 200).

People who have swine flu symptoms will be given a unique access number and told where their nearest antiviral collection point is. They should then ask a flu friend – a friend or relative who doesn't have swine flu – to go and pick up their antiviral from their nearest antiviral collection point. The flu friend must show their own ID as well as that of the patient.

Latest news – 12 November 2009
There were 64,000 new cases of swine flu in England last week, down nearly 25 per cent on the week before when there were 84,000 new cases.

Most new cases in the last week have been among the under-one and one to four age groups.

http://www.direct.gov.uk/swineflu/ (accessed 18 November 2009)

The Mental Capacity Act (MCA)

Deprivation of liberty safeguards (DOLs)

The Mental Capacity Act deprivation of liberty safeguards (formerly known as the Bournewood safeguards) were introduced into the Mental Capacity Act 2005 through the Mental Health Act 2007 (which received Royal Assent in July 2007).

The MCA DOL safeguards apply to anyone:

■ aged 18 and over

- who suffers from a mental disorder or disability of the mind – such as dementia or a profound learning disability
- who lacks the capacity to give informed consent to the arrangements made for their care and/or treatment and
- for whom deprivation of liberty (within the meaning of Article 5 of the ECHR) is considered after an independent assessment to be necessary in their best interests to protect them from harm.

The safeguards cover patients in hospitals and people in care homes registered under the Care Standards Act 2000, whether placed under public or private arrangements. The safeguards were implemented in April 2009.

The safeguards are designed to protect the interests of an extremely vulnerable group of service users and to:

- ensure people can be given the care they need in the least restrictive regimes
- prevent arbitrary decisions that deprive vulnerable people of their liberty
- provide safeguards for vulnerable people
- provide them with rights of challenge against unlawful detention
- avoid unnecessary bureaucracy

Reference

http://www.dh.gov.uk/; accessed 18 November 2009.

Mental Capacity Act (2005) Code of Practice

The Code of Practice (Code) provides guidance on how the Mental Capacity Act 2005 (Act) works on a day-to-day basis. It has case studies and explains in more detail what the key features of the law are. Certain categories of people have a legal duty to have regard to the Code. This includes:

- Professionals and anyone who is paid for the work they do in relation to people who lack capacity, e.g. doctors, nurses, social workers, care managers, solicitors, police officers, ambulance crew and paid carers
- Attorneys appointed under a Lasting Power of Attorney (LPA) or Enduring Power of Attorney (EPA)
- Deputies appointed by the Court of Protection (Court). Family, friends and unpaid carers do not have a duty to 'have regard' to the Code but will still find the guidance helpful.

Deprivation of liberty safeguards – Code of Practice

The deprivation of liberty safeguards (DOLs) were introduced into the Mental Capacity Act 2005 by the Mental Health Act 2007. They came into force in April 2009.

The safeguards provide a framework for approving the deprivation of liberty for people who lack the capacity to consent to treatment or care in either a hospital or care home that, in their own best interests, can only be provided in circumstances that amount to a deprivation of liberty.

The safeguards legislation contains detailed requirements about when and how deprivation of liberty may be authorised. It provides for an assessment process that must be undertaken before deprivation of liberty may be authorised and includes detailed arrangements for renewing and challenging the authorisation of deprivation of liberty.

The Code of Practice contains guidance on the deprivation of liberty safeguards. It is particularly intended to provide guidance for professionals involved in administering and delivering the safeguards, who are under a duty to have regard to the Code. The Code is also intended to provide information for people who are, or could become, subject to the deprivation of liberty safeguards, and for their families, friends and carers, as well as for anyone who believes that someone is being deprived of their liberty unlawfully.

Independent Mental Capacity Advocates' (IMCAs) roles and responsibilities

The MCA DOLs provide protection for vulnerable people accommodated in hospitals or care homes in circumstances that amount to a deprivation of their liberty, and who lack capacity to consent to the care or treatment they need. In such cases, the MCA DOLs provide a lawful way in which to care for people without their consent, provided that:

- it is in their own best interests
- it is necessary to keep them from harm
- it is a proportionate response to the likelihood and seriousness of harm.

Under the MCA DOLs, there are a number of circumstances when IMCAs must act. These include the following:

- when the hospital or care home has requested an assessment about depriving a person of their liberty, if there is no one else to represent that person the IMCA then serves to represent the person during the assessment process

- when a hospital or care home has deprived a person of their liberty and that person (or their representative) requests the support of an IMCA in order to ensure that they understand their rights
- where a hospital or care home has deprived a person of their liberty and there is (temporarily) nobody available to act as that person's representative.

References

http://www.publicguardian.gov.uk/; accessed 18 November 2009.
http://www.kent.gov.uk/; accessed 18 November 2009.

Discussion points

- Discuss with staff the importance of the deprivation of liberty safeguards.
- Discuss the role of the IMCAs within the care home.

Promoting care homes

Owing to the recession, the Government is faced with many financial challenges, and the care industry will inevitably have to adjust to the threat of severe financial constraints.

There has been much in the press regarding the future funding of the care sector and The English Community Care Association (ECCA) has issued a joint statement with Action on Elder Abuse that condemns the Government's plans to cut spending in the care sector in 2010 (Patterson, 2009).

Despite these plans, I believe passionately in the concept of care homes as the preferred option for the care of older people. Having worked in the NHS throughout the 1970s and 1980s I can remember the poor conditions on some of the long-stay 'Nightingale' wards which provided little privacy and dignity. Towards the end of the 1980s there was a transfer of older people to new purpose-built care homes that provided residents with the opportunity to be cared for in their own room, with modern shared-lounge facilities.

During my career I have seen tremendous improvements in the care sector, so I am annoyed at the Government's proposed spending cuts, especially when so much good has already been achieved.

The environmental standards of many care homes today are exceptional; with staff appearing dedicated, well trained and delivering high standards of care in safe, friendly, professional and secure facilities.

Meals are provided that form the basis of a balanced diet and residents are encouraged to take part in general social activities.

In many homes, residents enjoy 'state-of-the-art' bedrooms with *en suite* facilities, plasma screen TVs, WiFi Internet access, hairdressing salons, dining areas, mini-shops and large spacious lounges designed to meet their needs. This picture is a vast improvement on how things were in previous decades. I couldn't agree more with Gary Fitzgerald, Chief Executive of Action on Elder Abuse, who has said:

> Encouraging a reduction in the use of residential care in order to save money undermines the whole purpose of a needs assessment which involves personal choice, and should not be promoted as a solution to the funding challenges created by the recent Government proposals on long-term care.
>
> Such an option is clearly not about 'efficiency' savings based on the needs of the individual.
>
> With all the evidence indicating that older people are most at risk of abuse living in their own homes, it is surely time for a more sophisticated approach to this whole issue.

Those working in care homes must remain optimistic about the future delivery of care and promote their facilities as being the most suitable and protective environment for the care and support of older people. We need to promote our care homes at every opportunity in the media and in the local community.

Remaining silent is no longer an option if we are to continue to develop care home services to meet individual resident's needs.

References

Ashurst, A. (2009) Promoting care homes. *Nursing & Residential Care*, **11**(12), 535.

Patterson, M. (2009) *ECCA and AEA Condemn Residential Care Spending Cuts*. Available online at: http://www.ecca.org.uk/.

CHAPTER 11

The future challenges

Meeting future care challenges

The Prime Minister, Gordon Brown, acted quickly to address the many histori-cal, complex issues surrounding the development of the National Health Serv-ice, (NHS), and in doing so, provided hope to many NHS professionals. How-ever, I believe that the thousands of staff employed throughout the independent care sector deserve to be given some form of reassurance by the Government, who need to formally recognise the important role that these dedicated people play in their continuing partnership with the NHS.

Stephen O'Brien, MP, the Shadow Minister for Health spoke at the Care Home Forum on 'meeting the care challenges of the future'. In his thought-provoking speech delivered to 200 care home owners, managers and suppliers, the Shadow Minister outlined the key challenges facing the independent care sector.

The challenges and opportunities include: care funding, residents' personal dignity, care home regulation, providing a choice for residents and the continu-ing challenges that are facing its 'vast and dedicated workforce'. It appears that under a Conservative government, the aim would be to put the service user at the centre of their care. O'Brien stated: 'ultimately, care homes must, and in the majority of cases do, take responsibility for providing a service that confers the most dignity on the users'.

With regard to the regulation of care homes, some concerns about the merger of the Healthcare Commission and Commission for Social Care Inspec-tion (CSCI) were raised. O'Brien would not want to see CSCI subsumed by the Healthcare Commission. Care homes are not hospitals and should not be inspected as such. O'Brien also recognises the increased rates of dementia in older people and that; as a result, it will be essential in the future to have spe-cialist care homes situated across the country. It is important that people can be cared for in the long-term, near to their families and in a suitable environment.

Too many vulnerable people with mental illness and learning disabilities are, in the view presented by O'Brien, still being let down.

Care homes have a part to play in spreading and delivering best practice. With rising demand and a more demanding client base, it is clear that the care sector will change. Irrespective of the type of government this country has in the future, one fact remains clear: we owe it to the nation's older people and those with mental illness and learning disabilities to provide a consistently high standard of care. This care should be delivered in an appropriate environment by well trained and experienced nurses, therapists and carers that work in partnership with their NHS colleagues.

References

Ashurst, A. (2007) Meeting future care challenges. *Nursing & Residential Care*, **9**(7), 293.

Key points

- It appears that under a Conservative Government, the aim would be to put the service user at the centre of their care.
- Too many vulnerable people with mental illness and learning disabilities are, in the view presented by Stephen O'Brien, still being let down.
- We owe it to the nation's older people and those with mental illness and learning disabilities to provide a consistently high standard of care.

Discussion points

- How can we develop and improve the standards of care in our care homes?
- How can we develop and improve our partnership with our colleagues in the National Health Service (NHS)?
- How do we ensure that all our residents are provided with services that maximise their respect, privacy and dignity?

Organising regular outings for older people helps them enjoy a quality lifestyle.

Nursing degree: threat or opportunity?

The Nursing and Midwifery Council (NMC) has confirmed that, from 2013–14, students can only start pre-registration nursing programmes that meet the regulator's new approved standards. From the beginning of that academic year, the minimum level of education for new nurses will be degree level.

The NMC's Chief Executive and Registrar, Dickon Weir-Hughes, said: 'The public rightly expect to receive high-quality care from nurses. Raising the level of education is essential in ensuring that future nursing students are fully prepared to undertake the new roles and responsibilities that will be expected of them' (NMC, 2009).

The NMC has been quick to alleviate fears and concerns expressed by registered nurses by answering frequently asked questions on its website.

Does this mean that all nurses will need to have degrees?

The NMC (2009) has confirmed that this change only applies to new nurses undertaking pre-registration programmes.

Existing nurses will not be required to undertake degrees. Employers will need to consider, as they do now, whether they wish to support nurses without degrees to 'top-up'.

Employers will also need to consider any additional training that nurses may require in order to be effective mentors, particularly those in community settings who will be taking on students as part of their practice learning.

Will nurses without degrees be able to retain their registration?

Nurses who are already on the register will not need a degree in order to retain their registration.

Together with the other regulators, the NMC is exploring a system of revalidation so that nurses and midwives can demonstrate the knowledge and skills that they need in order to practise safely and effectively in the different roles they now undertake.

Therefore nurses must take personal responsibility to prepare for revalidation and continue to maintain their professional clinical learning and development.

Consultation

The public had the opportunity to respond to a national consultation that was open until the end of April 2010.

The more people that express their views on this important issue, the more the NMC will gain an accurate picture of how nurses actually feel about the future pathway of the profession.

I believe that registered nurses should not feel threatened, but should welcome the opportunity to maximise their professional, clinical and educational potential while remembering their commitment to those they care for.

References

Ashurst, A. (2009) Nursing degree: threat or opportunity? *Nursing & Residential Care*, **12**(1), 535.

http://www.nmc-uk.org/; accessed 1 December 2009.

Key points

- The Nursing and Midwifery Council (NMC) has confirmed that, from 2013–14, students can only start pre-registration nursing programmes that meet the regulator's new approved standards.
- The NMC (2009) has confirmed that this change only applies to new nurses undertaking pre-registration programmes.
- Nurses who are already on the register will not need a degree in order to retain their registration.

Discussion points

- In what manner can care home and hospital manager's implement a positive practical strategy for their staff who want to continue their continuing personal development?
- What practical suggestions are there for registered nurses who wish to return to university?
- How can managers continue to update themselves professionally?
- In the next five years I believe that nursing will change in a positive way, generating new educational challenges and provide the opportunity for all registered nurses to achieve their personal academic, managerial and clinical goals. Do your staff team agree or disagree with this statement?

Clinical governance

Clinical governance is a framework which helps all clinicians – including nurses – to continuously improve quality and safeguard standards of care (Royal College of Nursing, 1998).

Clinical governance definitions

In 1998 Sam Galbraith, the Scottish Minister for Health, outlined clinical governance as:

... the vital ingredient which will enable us to achieve a Health Service in which the quality of health care is paramount. The best definition that I have seen of clinical governance is simply that it means 'corporate accountability for clinical performance'. Clinical governance will not replace professional self regulation and individual clinical judgment, concepts that lie at the heart of health care in this country. But it will add an extra dimension that will provide the public with guarantees about standards of clinical care.

In 1998, Scally and Donaldson described clinical governance as:

A framework through which NHS organisations are accountable for continuously improving the quality of their services and safeguarding high standards of care by creating an environment in which excellence in clinical care will flourish.

The Department of Health white paper *A First Class Service: Quality in the New NHS* (DoH, 1998) also echoed this description, which aims to integrate recognised high standards of care, transparent responsibility and accountability for those standards, and a constant dynamic of improvement.

The Essence of Care (DoH, 2001) has been designed to support the measures to improve quality, set out in *A First Class Service*, and will contribute to the introduction of clinical governance at local level. The benchmarking process outlined in *The Essence of Care* helps practitioners to take a structured approach to sharing and comparing practice, enabling them to identify the best and to develop action plans to remedy poor practice.

There is no electronic version available for the 2001 edition of this document. However, the revised 2003 edition is available, containing subsequent additions.

Essence of Care: *patient-focused benchmarks for clinical governance*

DoH (2003) states:

This document contains the toolkit for benchmarking the fundamentals of care.

This includes the background to Essence of Care, a description of the benchmarking tool, how to use the benchmarks and record forms for developing action and business plans. Nine sets of benchmarks are also included. It is intended that health and social care personnel use this document to address issues of concern within their areas of work and to improve services already provided.

Care home managers can access the Department of Health website to keep themselves up to date in the developments of the *Essence of Care*.

The RCN (2003) states that:

The launch of clinical governance in 1998 placed quality at the centre of the NHS reforms.

Although it was introduced across the NHS, its principles apply equally across the independent sector, as shown by the creation of the Care Standards Act (2000). Clinical governance aims to integrate all the activities that impact on patient care into one strategy. This involves improving the quality of information, promoting collaboration, team working, and partnerships, as well as reducing variations in practice, and implementing evidence based practice.

The RCN (2003) has developed a number of key principles which underpin the implementation of clinical governance. These are based on the work of the Quality Improvement Programme, and have been refined in the light of recent policy initiatives:

- Clinical governance must be focused on improving the quality of patient care.
- Clinical governance should apply to all health care, wherever it is being delivered.
- Clinical governance demands true partnerships between all professional groups, between clinical staff and managers, and between patients and clinical staff.
- Public and patient involvement is an essential requirement for effective clinical governance.
- Nurses have a key role to play in the implementation of clinical governance.

References

Scally, G. and Donaldson, L. J. (1998) Clinical governance and the drive for quality improvement in the new NHS in England. *British Medical Journal*, **317**(7150), 61–5.

Department of Health (1998) *A First Class Service: Quality in the New NHS*. http://www.dh.gov.uk/; accessed 29 December 2009.

Clinical Governance: an RCN Resource (2003). Available at RCNONLINE: http://www.rcn.org.uk/. Accesses 29 December 2009.

Department of Health (2001) revised (2003) *The Essence of Care: Patient-focused Benchmarking for Health Care Practitioners*. DoH, London.

Department of Health (2006) *Essence of Care Benchmarks for Promoting Health*. http://www.dh.gov.uk/; accessed 29 December 2009.

National minimum standards

Today care home managers are responsible for meeting the national minimum standards as set out in *Care Homes for Older People: National Minimum Standards and the Care Home Regulations*, 3rd edn (Department of Health, 2003). This document contains a statement of national minimum standards published by the Secretary of State under section 23(1) of the Care Standards Act 2000.

The statement is applicable to care homes (as defined by section 3 of that Act) which provide accommodation, together with nursing or personal care, for older people. The regulations incorporate amendments made by S.I. 2002 No. 865. Stationery Office Publication, ISBN 011322607 1.

The full details of the National Care Standards can be found at http://dh.gov.uk/

Care Quality Commission

The Care Quality Commission is the independent regulator of health and social care in England. Its aim is to make sure better care is provided for everyone, whether in hospital, care homes, people's own homes, or elsewhere.

It regulates health and adult social care services, whether provided by the NHS, local authorities, private companies or voluntary organisations. It also seeks to protect the interests of people whose rights are restricted under the Mental Health Act.

New registration system

From April 2010, the regulation of health and adult social care will change. Legislation is bringing in a new registration system that applies to all regulated health and adult social care services.

The CQC website is the definitive source of information on the new registration system and will be regularly updated.

Why a new registration system?

Legislation is bringing in a new system that applies to all regulated health and adult social care services.

Registration is at the centre of the new system.

From April 2010, all health and adult social care providers who provide regulated activities are required by law to be registered with the Quality Care Commission. To do so, providers must show they are meeting new essential standards of quality and safety across all of the regulated activities they provide.

The new system will make sure that people can expect services to meet essential standards of quality and safety that respect their dignity and protect their rights.

The new system is focused on outcomes, rather than systems and processes, and places the views and experience of people who use services at the centre.

Subject to legislation, new registration comes into force on 1 April 2010 for NHS trusts (including primary care trusts as providers) and on 1 October 2010 for adult social care and independent healthcare providers (registration under the Care Standards Act 2000 continues until 30 September 2010).

How do providers make sure they comply with the new regulations?

To register with the CQC, providers must demonstrate they meet the new essential standards of quality and safety across all the services they provide.

By law, the CQC is required to produce guidance about compliance with the new regulations. The guidance applies to all health and adult social care providers. It describes quality and safety from the perspective of people who use services and places them at the centre of the registration system. The guidance focuses on people rather than policies; on outcomes rather than systems. It relates to important aspects of care such as:

- involvement and information
- personalised care and treatment
- safety and safeguarding

Essential standards of quality and safety make clear the outcomes the CQC expects people to experience if the provider is compliant with the new regulations. It also gives prompts that providers may wish to use to consider if they have the building blocks in place to achieve good outcomes.

Where there is evidence of adverse outcomes the CQC will have to look at the systems and processes of due diligence in consideration of the regulatory action they need to take to protect people's safety, dignity and rights. The CQC will be targeted and proportionate in all its activities.

The **Judgment framework** is the document that CQC inspectors will use to judge compliance with the regulations.

The CQC will publish this as part of the guidance in direct response to its consultation on the original guidance in which people asked for more detail on how the CQC would make judgments about compliance.

It has a strong focus on involving people in the development of local services, ensuring their voices are heard, and respecting people's dignity and rights. It includes case studies from different service types and outlines how its approach will be targeted and proportionate to levels of risk.

How will the CQC use the guidance about compliance?

The CQC will use the guidance about compliance to consider:

- whether a provider continues to be suitable and is allowed to keep its registration
- how the CQC will judge compliance of a provider with the essential standards of quality and safety
- whether concerns about a provider should require them to make improvements or should lead to the CQC using their more formal powers which include restricting, suspending or in the most serious cases removing their registration

The CQC also wants to make sure that people who use services are empowered to use the guidance and for it to be a tool for them to trigger improvement themselves.

Managers are advised to keep up to date about all the work of the Care Quality Commission by means of regular visits to the website: http://www.cqc.org.uk/.

Afterword

This book has been written to help those who wish to develop their own management potential and the potential of others.

One of the best aspects of a care home manager's role is to discover staff who have potential. Encouraging and motivating people who are keen to learn can give the manager a great amount of job satisfaction.

The most successful managers inspire their team members. I believe that people want to work alongside managers who are passionate about what they do.

Reflection is useful in order that we can learn from our mistakes. I would recommend that all potential leaders actually keep a reflective diary.

Remember the importance of trying to achieve a true work–life balance. There is the possibility that care home managers believe that they have to be on duty every hour of the day. It is really important to delegate when the opportunity arises.

May I take this opportunity to wish you well in your personal quest to develop your self and others to achieve success and happiness in your future management career?

I hope that reading this book has inspired you to consider a career in management; we will always need well-trained, valued, committed and dedicated bedside nurses. However, there will always be the need for experienced managers who are able to utilise their skills and maximise the available care home resources.

Index